Supervision:

A Handbook for Success

About the Authors

Bruce B. Tepper is a noted speaker, trainer, and consultant in management.

Adapted for the American Correctional Association by **Ida M. Halasz,** Ph.D., who served as the Deputy Administrator of the National Institute of Corrections Academy, U.S. Department of Justice. Currently, as Vice President of Powell International Inc., she provides training and consulting services to public and private sector organizations.

ISBN 1-56991-089-8

Foreword

Corrections has evolved from the days when staff were thought of as "guards." Today, corrections is a legitimate and recognized profession. The modern correctional climate expects and demands unique workplace standards from the men and women called upon each day to serve their organizations. Correctional staff use specialized knowledge, skills and abilities that have become the key to an increased regard from around the world. Indeed, the role of the *correctional supervisor* is linked to successful outcomes in meeting or exceeding the mission of an organization.

Good supervisors, in any occupation, find themselves becoming coaches, mentors, disciplinarians, time and attendance managers, budget monitors, and referees. Correctional supervisors must do all of these tasks while at the same time ensuring that staff levels are maintained—and that a spirit of mutual respect is cultivated among both staff and offenders. How is this accomplished? The answer, of course, is through adequate preparation and training.

Promotional opportunities and upward mobility in correctional organizations have created a cadre of young, often inexperienced supervisors. These staff members suddenly find themselves in the role of supervising others in a division, section, or unit. Facility CEOs are committed, fortunately, to helping those staff members prepare for their new jobs.

This self-paced workbook should be considered a vital part of that academic preparation. It should be used as an important tool to those accepting the challenges of correctional supervision. New supervisors must be willing and able to recognize the importance of their new responsibilities, and this workbook will, undoubtedly, help them.

Aristedes W. Zavaras, Executive Director
Colorado Department of Corrections

a publication of the
AMERICAN CORRECTIONAL ASSOCIATION
206 North Washington Street, Suite 200
Alexandria, VA 22314
703-224-0000
1-800-ACA-Join
www.aca.org

Introduction

Congratulations on your position as a supervisor. If this is *your first opportunity to supervise* the activity of others, you're undoubtedly looking forward to the experience.

For many, supervising others brings a mix of anticipation and fear. There is the promotion to the new position itself, the opportunity to teach others and share your knowledge, and a new sense of authority and control.

There is also the fear of having to depend on others to do the work, of getting their respect and attention, and of being responsible for what others do.

You'll find that there is no magic to being a good or even great supervisor. It takes some understanding of human behavior—how people act—combined with the timely application of effective management skills.

This workbook will help you make some sense of your new responsibilities. It will help you develop your own program for success.

If you are a *seasoned veteran*, this workbook will provide you with some new approaches and ideas. It will help reinforce your efforts to become an even better supervisor.

You're on the way to learning and using the tools that will ensure your success as an effective supervisor—a supervisor who is sought after by management and respected by staff.

Self-Assessment

How do you rate your supervising ability? This self-assessment will reaffirm your strengths and identify areas for improvement. In either case, it is a starting point for becoming a highly effective supervisor. For each statement, check off the category that best describes you.

	Always	Sometimes	Never	Score
I feel comfortable in a leadership position.	❑	❑	❑	_____
I am well organized in my activities.	❑	❑	❑	_____
I plan my work activities in advance.	❑	❑	❑	_____
I am comfortable making decisions.	❑	❑	❑	_____
I can handle more than one project at a time.	❑	❑	❑	_____
I organize my time well.	❑	❑	❑	_____
I have good written communication skills.	❑	❑	❑	_____
I have good oral communication and presentation skills.	❑	❑	❑	_____
I am comfortable "selling" my ideas to others.	❑	❑	❑	_____
People see me as a leader in group activities.	❑	❑	❑	_____
I am a good teacher; people learn from me easily.	❑	❑	❑	_____
I have a good understanding of people and am patient when working with others.	❑	❑	❑	_____
I am comfortable sharing the workload with others.	❑	❑	❑	_____

	Always	Sometimes	Never	Score
I am willing to take responsibility for the actions of others.	❑	❑	❑	_____
I am willing to put in extra hours on the job when necessary.	❑	❑	❑	_____
I enjoy solving problems involving human behavior.	❑	❑	❑	_____
I can focus on long-range problems as well as day-to-day problems to help find solutions.	❑	❑	❑	_____
			Total Score	_____

Scoring the Self-Assessment

To determine your score, give yourself a 3 for each *Always*, a 2 for each *Sometimes*, and a 1 for each *Never*. Now go back and get your total score. Let's see how you did:

42 or Higher
Excellent skills.

33—42
Better than average but with room for improvement.

24—32
Average performance for a supervisor with several years' experience.

32 or fewer
Not unusual for the new supervisor.

Take a serious look at the *Nevers* and the *Sometimes* and make efforts at improving them. Also, make a commitment to continue focusing on the *Always* issues.

Will this workbook make you an effective supervisor immediately? No—neither a workbook nor a training session can do that. It takes consistent effort on your part. Supervision is as much an art as it is a science. But with practice and experience, you'll develop skills for handling the wide variety of challenges you're likely to encounter.

Table of Contents

Chapter One

The Role of the New Supervisor

Chapter Two

Leadership Skills

Chapter Three

Decision-Making Skills

Chapter Four

Managing Change

Chapter Five

Managing Your Time

Chapter Six

Communicating Effectively

Chapter Seven

Making Meetings Productive

Chapter Eight

Praise, Criticism, and Conflict

Chapter Nine

Delegating Work

Chapter Ten

The Complete Supervisor

Chapter One

THE ROLE OF THE NEW SUPERVISOR

Chapter Objectives

After completing this chapter, you should be able to:

- Describe the overall role of the supervisor.
- Develop personal plans and work plans for success.
- Decide how to put your plans into action.

Maria has worked as a correctional officer for over four years and has just been promoted to a shift supervisor position. She believes her promotion was the result of her attention to detail and her excellent attendance record. Although she's never had management or supervisory training of any kind, she is excited as well as nervous about her new assignment. The promotion was a great opportunity. Now Maria is beginning to think about her new job and her career prospects. Later in the chapter, we will rejoin Maria and learn how she develops an action plan for work.

As a supervisor, you do your job by creating output—getting work done—through the efforts of others.

The New Supervisor: Getting Started

The role of the supervisor is, of course, "supervision." As a supervisor, you do your job by creating output—getting work done—through the efforts of others.

Your specific duties as a supervisor can include any or all of the following.

- Planning activities, hours, and scheduling.
- Providing leadership and direction.
- Managing or supervising others to make sure that work gets done.
- Taking responsibility for the performance of the people working for you.

How do you begin? Getting started as a supervisor begins with both personal and work planning. If your work and personal plans don't mesh, it's time to come up with a new strategy.

Critical Questions for Planning

Take time now to develop your personal and work goals. Remember that a goal is something to aim for, something you want to achieve. It's a clear statement of desired behavior. According to management expert Ken Blanchard, goals should be:

S *Specific.* Goals are stated in descriptive terms, not in generalities. In other words, you can "see the behavior."

M *Measurable.* Goals include dates and other items that can be measured, or quantified.

A *Attainable* or *Achievable.* You are capable of doing them.

R *Realistic.* They are possible to do or achieve.

T *Timely.* You have the time available to do them.

For example, instead of saying "I want to buy a car," a valuable goal statement might be, "I will

- purchase a _____—*add the type of car you want, including whether it will be a new or used*—car
- by next _____—*you specify the date*— with a
- down payment of _____ , —*you specify how much you have for a*

down payment—

- a loan from _____,—*you specify who will give you the loan and whether you have been approved for it yet—*
- and a maximum payment per month of _____." —*you specify how much you can afford to pay for a car loan per month.*

Take a Moment . . .

What Are My Personal Goals?

Check the statements that apply to you and then make them into **SMART** goals.

- ☐ Own my home

  ____

- ☐ Have a family

  ____

- ☐ Buy a new car

  ____

- ☐ Advance within the organization

  ____

- ☐ Earn more money

  ____

- ☐ Have more prestige

  ____

- ☐ Take a vacation

  ____

- ☐ Other(s):

  ____

Take a Moment *(continued)*

What Are the Business Goals for My Department and for Me as a New Supervisor?

Check off your department's goals as well as your own. Then make sure that they are **SMART** goals. If you have any difficulty developing the goals, discuss them with your supervisor.

- ☐ Earn the respect of my staff

  ____

  ____

- ☐ Eliminate problem situations

  ____

  ____

- ☐ Assert my authority

  ____

  ____

- ☐ Contribute great new ideas

  ____

  ____

- ☐ Change procedures and methods (over which I have authority)

  ____

  ____

- ☐ Other(s):

  ____

  ____

  ____

  ____

Take a Moment *(continued)*

Do My Goals Mesh?

Now, list the goals in order of priority to be achieved next year. Do your work goals mesh with your personal goals? In other words, are they compatible with each other?

Personal Goals:	Work Goals:
1. ______________	1. ______________
2. ______________	2. ______________
3. ______________	3. ______________
4. ______________	4. ______________
5. ______________	5. ______________
6. ______________	6. ______________
7. ______________	7. ______________
8. ______________	8. ______________
9. ______________	9. ______________
10. ______________	10. ______________

What Action Must I Take to Get My Ideas and Plans Accepted?

What actions do you have to take to achieve your goals? Complete the statement for those that apply. Add statements that are missing.

☐ Get staff support by:

____

☐ Convince senior management by:

____

☐ Convince my supervisor by:

____

☐ Convince myself by:

____

☐ Other(s):

____

____

Of these *actions*, which one seems most *crucial* to you?

____

If your personal and work goals clash, you may have to choose between them or decide to modify one or the other. The key is to have a plan so that you know exactly where you are headed. As a famous children's story says, "If you don't know where you're headed, how will you know when you get there?"

Personality Traits of the Successful Supervisor

Managers and supervisors need a variety of personality traits or characteristics to be successful. As a supervisor, you should be aware of which traits you see in yourself and which traits you might be able to improve on.

Check the traits that you see in yourself:

- ☐ Patience
- ☐ Tolerance
- ☐ Sensitivity
- ☐ Empathy
- ☐ Punctuality
- ☐ Decisiveness

These are just a few personality traits for you to consider. What other traits do you think effective supervisors need?

____

____

____

____

What areas do you need to improve on?

____

____

____

____

____

Barriers to Success

What barriers or pitfalls can prevent your success as a supervisor? Check the barriers that may apply to you:

- ☐ Too many goals
- ☐ Lack of priorities
- ☐ Incomplete projects
- ☐ Lack of self-confidence
- ☐ Other(s):

____

____

We often feel frustrated in our attempts to reach new goals because of barriers such as those above. In the remaining chapters, we'll discuss ways to overcome typical barriers to success.

Your Action Plan as a Supervisor

Complete the personal and work action plan on the next page. This is the first step toward becoming an effective supervisor. Your action plans will guide you through the day and help you achieve the personal and work goals that you developed in this chapter.

Supervisor's Action Plan

1. **List, in order of priority, the goals you've set for your department/unit over the next year.**

_______________ _______________

_______________ _______________

_______________ _______________

_______________ _______________

2. **List the steps needed to accomplish one of these goals.**

Goal: _______________

Step 1: _______________

Step 2: _______________

Step 3: _______________

3. **Explore your resources.** For each goal, what will you or your department/unit need to achieve it? For example, additional training may be needed for staff on how to conduct effective, consistent pat searches. _______________

____

____

4. **Evaluate your own or your department's/unit's ability to attain each goal.** Your job description and duties are a good place to start. (Write your own job description and list of duties if your organization doesn't have one). _______________

____

____

5. **Develop a way to measure and monitor progress toward each of your goals.** In other words, how will you evaluate success or shortcomings? _______________

____

____

Putting the Action Plan to Work

Now, what about putting the action plan to work? Let's return to Maria, our new shift supervisor in the correctional facility, to see what she does.

- In setting her goals, Maria is careful to make them **S**pecific, **M**easurable, **A**ttainable, **R**ealistic, and **T**imely:

Unreasonable Goals	**Reasonable Goals**
Decrease staff-inmate incident reports	Decrease staff-inmate reports by a specified amount and date
Get everyone to like me	Earn the respect of my staff by a specified time period and by modeling specified behaviors
Improve staff skills	Teach staff specified skills according to detailed plan and by the specified date

- Maria established the goal of decreasing staff-inmate incident reports by 10 percent over the next year. This is her number one goal, and it fits well into Maria's overall personal and departmental goals. She feels strongly that she can do it.

What steps might Maria take to make her goal a reality? The steps could include letting her staff know it's a priority for their performance ratings, convincing the organization to recognize the improvements, and improving the interpersonal communication skills of staff through training.

Can Maria succeed in her goal? This will greatly depend on whether or not she follows through with the performance appraisals and training for staff, including on-the-job training. What other resources might she need?

- Maria decides to improve the interpersonal communication skills of staff. The steps she decides to take in order to make her goal happen are:

  1. Determine the specific skills her staff needs—verbal and nonverbal communication, teamwork, etc.

2. Determine where and how those skills can be learned—workshops, videotapes, self-instructional courses, etc.
3. Determine which method or program will best meet her staff's needs.
4. Evaluate her resources.
   a. Is this goal in the scope of her job and duties?
   b. Will the organization allocate the necessary resources?
   c. Will the staff have the time?
   d. Will the staff share her motivation and have a reason to improve? (If not, Maria will need to examine this problem as a separate issue.)
5. Break the training task down into its components.
   a. Select the best method for her department.
   b. Convince staff and management with supporting reasons that this method is the best choice.
   c. Determine who will go through the program, then schedule training.
6. Set up a method to evaluate the effects of her training program.
   a. Determine everyone's staff-inmate incident record.
   b. Identify the number and type of grievances.
   c. Observe whether staff are applying the new skills. If they are not, determine the reasons why and seek ways to motivate these staff.

Now that Maria has her plan all mapped out, she can get started and make modifications or changes as needed.

In Conclusion

Let's review the basics of getting started in a supervisory job:

1. Determine personal and work goals for a one-year period and a five-year period.
2. Determine resources for reaching those goals. (What new skills, abilities, and ideas will you need?)
3. Break down and prioritize your goals.
4. Get support for your goals from your staff and supervisor.
5. Make decisions and develop and implement a plan to reach your goals.

Chapter One Review

1. True/False. As a supervisor, you must get work done through others.
2. List two common duties of a supervisor.

   ____

   ____

3. Define the term goal.

   ____

   ____

4. List four personality traits a supervisor needs.

   ____

   ____

   ____

   ____

5. List two common barriers to succeeding as a supervisor.

   ____

   ____

Chapter Two

LEADERSHIP SKILLS

Chapter Objectives

After completing this chapter, you should be able to:

- Evaluate the needs of your staff.
- Assess your leadership skills.
- Identify ways to establish and exercise authority.

Carlos started as a clerical worker at the state department of corrections about three years ago. Everyone liked Carlos and felt he was good at his job. His supervisor was promoted, and Carlos was offered the position of supervising six other clerical workers—including some who have become his good friends.

Although Carlos took a couple of management courses in school, he is still very concerned about his ability to lead others. He's a bit worried about how to work with people who are his friends as well as coworkers. Carlos wanted this position very much. In fact, his goals include advancing to management. Now that he's arrived, how can he win the respect of his staff and feel comfortable leading them?

Friendship Above Responsibility?

If you've been promoted from within, it's time to take stock of your new role. Your former "equals" may, in some cases, resent your promotion. Others may feel that as your friend, you will give them favorable assignments or excuse unacceptable work habits.

Therefore, you must establish your position quickly. Your first duty is to do your job and do it well. This often means that co-workers will no longer be close friends. You cannot put friendship above responsibility. That does not mean that people will turn their backs on you. Many will be proud and happy for you and will do everything they can to support you in your new role. But do not stake your future on trying to stay friends with everyone and being a success as a supervisor at the same time. It is very hard to do.

The key to making a successful transition in the same workplace is to be clear about your own duties and responsibilities and about how best to perform your job.

. . . leadership is getting others to want to follow your direction and be productive in doing so.

The Skills of Leadership

Establishing your new role begins with a very vague term: *leadership*. Essentially, leadership is getting others to want to follow your direction and be productive in doing so.

Here are the *skills* necessary for leadership in most fields. Check those that you feel you currently have:

- ☐ Confident in your ability
- ☐ Communicate effectively
- ☐ Able to make decisions
- ☐ Trust your staff to do the job
- ☐ Desire to develop skills in others
- ☐ Comfortable giving direction to others
- ☐ Able to motivate people

☐ List other traits:

____

____

Why are these skills and traits important? Let's take a closer look at each one.

Confidence is important because:

- Others won't feel confident in a leader who lacks confidence.
- It subtly demonstrates your right to authority.
- It makes your staff feel comfortable that there is direction and purpose for what they do.

Good communication skills are essential to:

- Clearly explain tasks and objectives to your staff.
- Provide guidance and direction on completing those tasks.
- Explain your actions to your supervisor(s) effectively.

Making decisions is critical for:

- Keeping the workflow moving.
- Quickly settling what could become major "personality" issues.
- Keeping the effort of all staff flowing in the same direction.

Senior staff often cite their *ability to make decisions* as the main reason for their *success*.

Trusting your staff is essential for:

- The organization to grow and expand.

- You and your staff to become more productive.
- Developing more skilled talent from within.

A desire to develop skills in others:

- Helps staff develop their own talents.
- Helps you tolerate mistakes that allow for growth and learning.
- Helps you be a teacher as well as a supervisor—a person willing to share growth and recognition with others.

Feeling comfortable in giving direction to others:

- Is essential to getting the work done.
- Helps show your staff that you are confident, in charge, and a good leader.
- Conveys that you trust others to complete tasks successfully.

Motivation

One leadership skill, motivation, deserves a closer look, because all other skills depend on this one. People are motivated by different needs:

- Security
- Recognition
- A sense of accomplishment
- Money
- Social aspects of their job

Effective supervisors learn to recognize these traits and use the appropriate motivation with each staff member.

As a supervisor, do not assume that everyone shares your goals and desires. Not everyone wants the "headaches" of supervising. Many prefer to do the best possible work in their current job. It's your job to learn what each of your staff members wants out of work and what is important to him or her.

. . . do not assume that everyone shares your goals and desires.

Many supervisors and managers assume that their staff are driven by a desire for more money. However, extensive research over the years has shown that money is usually not one of the top motivators. Surprised?

Take a Moment . . .

What motivator do you think is more important to people than money?

____

____

____

____

____

____

Compare your answers to the research findings on the next page.

What's more important to most people is:

- Recognition for doing a good job
- Opportunities for advancement
- Trust
- Responsibility
- Respect

Steps for Determining Staff Needs

Let's take a few moments now to determine your current staff needs.

Using the following worksheet, determine the needs of the people who work for you. Continue on a separate sheet of paper if necessary.

1. List each staff member and, from your perspective, write down what you believe are his or her top job goals.
2. Ask each staff member what his or her goals are and compare the answers to your list. If you see a discrepancy, adjust your list and determine which goals are the best match. Some staff members may not have clearly defined goals or may prefer to tell you what they think you want to hear. Writing goals down avoids these problems.
3. List the steps you believe you can take to best meet each staff member's needs. Take into account your supervisory style (your way of supervising).

Worksheet

Staff Member 1
Name: ______________________________

Staff member's view of goals:

____

My view of his/her job goals:

____

Best course of action:

____

Staff Member 2
Name: ______________________________

Staff member's view of goals:

____

My view of his/her goals:

____

Best course of action:

____

Staff Member 3
Name: ______________________________

Staff member's view of goals:

____

My view of his/her goals:

____

Best course of action:

____

Establishing and Exercising Authority

The power of leadership authority is derived (gained) in three basic ways:

1. Situations occur that require leadership, and through a general consensus, one individual earns that recognition from the group. The leader assumes control.

2. Specific activities or projects require a leader—often the person with the most skills or experience. Skill or experience is frequently a factor in the promotion of a new supervisor.

3. The title or position demands respect and recognition. For example, a line worker must take orders from and recognize the authority of a supervisor or manager—be it a sergeant, a lieutenant, a captain, or the superintendent or warden.

   Remember that titles can provide leadership, but they don't guarantee that the leader has any leadership skills.

   If you depend on your position for authority alone, you're likely to see a high turnover in your workforce and a lack of productivity. Durable and solid leadership can be established through a combination of methods. A true leader is a person whom people want to follow because they trust and respect that individual.

Moving Forward

Based on the broad skills outlined in this chapter, list the leadership skills you need to work on:

____

____

____

____

Check this list again when you've completed the workbook, and plan to spend more time on any areas that you still believe are weak. This may include additional reading or training.

Chapter Two Review

1. Define the term leadership.

 ____

 ____

 ____

2. List four skills of leadership.

 ____

 ____

 ____

 ____

3. List the top five job motivators for most people.

 ____

 ____

 ____

 ____

 ____

4. True/False. The higher the rank and title of a person, the better the leadership skills.

Chapter Three

DECISION-MAKING SKILLS

Chapter Objectives

After completing this chapter, you should be able to:

- Describe how to approach a decision with an open mind.
- Use a decision planner to evaluate the likely results of a decision.
- Prepare to "sell" decisions to the people they affect.

Decision making is an essential part of any supervisory job.

As shift supervisor at a residential center for youth, Joan is faced with many decisions on a daily basis. These decisions range from scheduling her staff's hours and determining their work assignments to participating in the quality committee with other supervisors and making suggestions for center operations. Joan is irritated by having to settle what she feels are minor disputes between staff members, particularly in the area of work assignments. It seems that whatever she does, someone is unhappy with her decision. She often feels that it would be easier just to ignore these disputes and hope the problems go away. Later in the chapter, we will see what decision Joan makes and how it affects her staff and the center.

Focusing on Decisions

Decision making is an essential part of any supervisory job. In fact, many administrators or senior managers consider it their primary responsibility.

Decision making is also one of the most difficult tasks for many new supervisors. When you were a frontline staff member, you had decisions made for you. Policy and direction of work were not your major concern.

As a supervisor, however, the situation is different. You should keep the following thoughts on decision making in mind.

- **Decision making is an essential part of supervising others.** Be careful not to trivialize decisions that may be of great importance to your staff.
- **Not all of your decisions will be the right ones.** Everyone makes mistakes, including CEOs of large companies and those in charge of correctional agencies and facilities.
- **Failing to take any action at all is also a decision.** "Deciding not to decide" carries the same risks and rewards as any other decision.

Keeping an Open Mind

How can you make good decisions as often as possible? You must be well informed. Good decisions result from gathering information. The five key steps to approaching a decision are:

Good decisions result from gathering information.

1. **Be truly open-minded.** Don't take sides or make judgments until you can examine all the information. Be aware that in many cases, you will be required to make a decision without complete information. Make the best possible decision with as much information as you can get.
2. **Avoid taking sides.** Don't assume that because one side in a dispute has a better track record than the other, that side will

always be right. Taking sides is not only unfair to everyone involved but also can lead to a poor decision.

3. **Recognize your own biases (preferences).** If we all saw things the same way, there would be no disputes or issues to resolve. The reality is that "obvious truths" are only obvious to those who believe them to be true. What seems obvious to you as a supervisor may not be obvious to your staff. Your perspective is different.

4. **Don't let titles or prestige influence your decision.** An individual's title may not be indicative of a person's skill or experience. You must make decisions based on the merit of the situation, not the title or image of the people involved.

5. **Avoid "absolute" wording in your decision.** Words such as *always* or *never* should be avoided. Situations are rarely that permanent. Instead, qualify the conditions that affect your decisions. For example, rather than say, "There always are . . .; therefore," you might say, "During the past month . . .; therefore, during the next month . . . will be implemented, and we will evaluate how it works."

Questions to Ask When Making a Decision

Ask yourself these four critical questions as you set out to make a decision:

1. Do I have enough information to make a decision?

2. Does the problem require a decision?

3. Am I the best person to make this decision?
4. What will be the worst possible result if I make a wrong decision?

Take a Moment . . .

Describe a decision (large or small) that you are facing.

____

____

Now ask yourself the four critical questions below. Write down your answers.

1. Do I have enough information to make a decision?

   ____

   ____

2. Does the problem require a decision?

   ____

   ____

3. Am I the best person to make this decision?

   ____

   ____

4. If I make a wrong decision, what will be the worst possible result?

   ____

Evaluating Your Decisions

Decisions are not made in a vacuum. Each decision you make affects other people and future decisions. On the next page is a *decision planner* to help you chart the affect that your decisions will have on the future. With practice, this process can become part of every decision you make.

Decision Planner

Problem
Clearly stated and defined:

____

Long-Range Effects

1. How long will/should the decision be in effect?

   ____

2. Can it be changed or reversed if necessary?

   ____

3. What are the most likely results of the decision?

   ____

4. What is the worst-case scenario that could result?

   ____

   ____

5. Is the worst-case scenario acceptable? Why or why not?

   ____

   ____

Influences on Others
Who else will be affected by the decision? Who else should be involved in making the decision.

Affected by Decision:	Involved in Decision:
________________	________________
________________	________________
________________	________________
________________	________________

Who else should be informed of the decision?

____

Agency Policies and Procedures

1. Does the decision contradict or change current organizational policy?

   ____

2. Does the decision fit the style and philosophy of the organization?

   ____

3. Does the organization have whatever resources are needed to implement the decision?

   ____

4. What will the financial influence of the decision be?

   ____

   ____

5. Who will be designated to carry out the decision?

   ____

   ____

Uniqueness of the Problem

1. Is the problem truly unique and not addressed by other policies and procedures?

   ____

   ____

2. Is the situation likely to occur again, requiring long-range thinking?

   ____

   ____

3. Is the decision creating new policy for the organization?

   ____

   ____

The Decision-Making Process

In any decision, you have three options:

1. Proceed (Yes).
2. Oppose (No).
3. Take no action at all and "let the problem solve itself."

Even a "good" decision could have negative consequences if it contradicts the organization's style and philosophy.

Note that the third choice is a decision as well. When you use the decision planner, list the possible results of taking no action, just as you would for a "Yes" or "No" decision.

Making decisions on the job is not always done in a perfect environment. As a supervisor, you must be concerned about the organization's culture and philosophy. Even a "good" decision could have negative consequences if it contradicts the organization's style and philosophy.

Risk Avoidance vs. Moving Forward

For that reason, most people make decisions on the basis of *risk avoidance*. They ask themselves, "What choice carries the least risk?" As you make decisions, though, bear in mind that risk avoidance in decision making may prevent you from trying innovative solutions and ideas. That is why the decision planner asks for the worst-case scenario resulting from your decision. It may well be worth some risk to move the organization forward.

Management texts for years have suggested waiting to make decisions until all the needed information has been obtained. In an ideal world, you would. Unfortunately, decisions must often be made quickly and without all the facts, which requires working with assumptions in some cases. Make sure that you know which information you are assuming and which information is fact when you make decisions.

Make sure that you know which information you are assuming and which information is fact when you make decisions.

The keys to moving forward in a decision are to:

1. Break the decision down into the smallest possible parts.
2. Use the decision planner to determine the range of likely results and whether you can accept them.

Decision Making in Action

How would Joan, the residential center supervisor, make a decision?

Sally and Jim, two of Joan's staff, seem to fight constantly over everything, sometimes disrupting other staff. Joan has decided that this disruptive behavior must end. After using the decision planner to develop a solution, Joan decided to move Jim to another department in the center.

Now what? That decision will require Joan and/or other staff to:

- Convince Jim of the benefit of the change.
- Convince a new supervisor to create a position and accept Jim.
- Convince Joan's manager to accept the decision.
- Find a replacement for Jim.
- Have the replacement meet with Sally and make sure that they get along.

- Notify personnel and/or any other departments who need to know about the change.
- Provide training for the new staff member.
- Post a job opening or advertisement to find the new staff member.

Even though Joan may not be personally responsible for all of these tasks, the simple decision to move Jim carries all these implications. Thus, decision making doesn't end with the decision in most cases. Action will be required to implement a decision.

Gaining Acceptance for the Decision

Supervisors must be prepared to promote, or "sell" their decisions.

Supervisors must be prepared to promote, or "sell" their decisions. Most decisions you make will affect people. There are four potential groups of people who will be affected by decisions you make:

1. Your immediate supervisor.
2. Other supervisors.
3. Staff directly affected by the decision.
4. Staff indirectly affected by the decision.

Before Joan transfers Jim to another department, she will also need assurance that Jim can work with the staff around him.

Preparing to "Sell" a Decision

How do you prepare to "sell" a decision you've made? Six key questions to ask when promoting a decision are:

1. What information should be provided to those people affected?
2. Should it be in writing, and, if so, how should I organize the information?
3. Is my presentation of the decision phrased in language that will gain support for the decision?
4. What negative responses might I expect?
5. When and how will the information be presented to the staff involved?
6. What questions are likely to come from supervisors and other staff when I present the decision?

Time and Method of Presenting Your Ideas

The timing and method of presenting your ideas can make a great deal of difference. Think about the best time and method to present your decision. In your organization, is new information usually presented in formal memos, all-desk announcements, or in one-on-one conversations?

The timing and method of presenting your ideas can make a great deal of difference.

Depending on the situation, does the decision need to be delivered to everyone, or just to the individuals involved?

Take a Moment . . .

Think about a decision you'll soon have to make, or one that you've made recently, and what you'll need to do to gain acceptance for it.

Ask yourself the six key questions and write your answers here:

1. What information should be provided to those people affected?

____

____

____

2. Should it be in writing, and, if so, how should I organize the information?

____

____

3. If my presentation of the decision phrased is in writing, will its language help me gain support for the decision?

____

4. What negative responses might I expect?

____

____

____

5. When and how will the information be presented to the staff involved? ______________________________

____

____

6. What questions are likely to come from supervisors and other staff when I present the decision? ____________________

____

____

In Conclusion

Decision making is an important part of every supervisor's job. It is a process that involves some risk—risk that is key to trying innovative solutions and ideas. Even taking no action at all is a decision, which involves some risk and has definite consequences.

Even taking no action at all is a decision, which involves some risk and has definite consequences.

Chapter Three Review

1. List the five steps to approaching a decision.

   ____

   ____

   ____

   ____

   ____

2. What questions should you ask yourself as you prepare to make a decision?

   ____

   ____

   ____

   ____

   ____

   ____

3. What are the three options in the decision making process?

   ____

   ____

   ____

4. List six key questions to ask when you're "selling" a decision.

____

____

____

____

____

____

Chapter Four

MANAGING CHANGE

Chapter Objectives

After completing this chapter, you should be able to:

- Describe why it's important to accept change.
- Explain how to implement change.
- Explain the importance of promoting the need for change.

Don is an office manager for a private corrections company. His company is growing rapidly, adding new people and building new facilities. Because of this growth, combined with ever-changing government regulations affecting his company's policies and procedures, Don feels as if he's in a constant state of change.

Every time Don's company designs new forms or methods, they seem to be out of date. A constant blizzard of paperwork affects Don and everyone in his department. There are always new ways to do things and new forms to complete. Several valuable staff have left in frustration. Later in the chapter, we'll learn some of the things Don can do to cope with the many changes he is facing.

Change is one of the most difficult aspects of work or life for many people to accept.

Accepting Change

Change is inevitable. What worked in the past or, for that matter, what works today may not work tomorrow.

Change is one of the most difficult aspects of work or life for many people to accept. By nature, most humans seek consistency and familiarity. The majority of people are not risk-takers or adventurers, so change is uncomfortable. Each time change occurs, our confidence level drops. After we finally perfect a task, or accept an idea, we have to start all over again.

Review your goals and objectives from Chapter One. As you'll see below, change can have a direct influence on goals.

Take a Moment . . .

The Influence of Change on My Goals

1. Personal Goals—Long-range and Short-range
   List the assumptions around which you built your plans. For example, if one of your goals is to buy a new car, what assumptions are you making about events beyond your control? Getting an annual raise, avoiding emergencies that could eat into your cash reserves, or feeling assured that your rent will not increase are some influences beyond your control.

Personal Goals	Noncontrollable Events That Could Affect the Goals
______________	______________
______________	______________
______________	______________
______________	______________

2. Work Goals
   Repeat the process with your work goals.

Work Goals	Noncontrollable Events That Could Affect the Goals
______________	______________
______________	______________
______________	______________
______________	______________

The Challenge of Change

Changes can and will occur in technology, legislation, societal attitudes and behaviors, personal wants and needs, management and supervisory techniques, organization-staff relationships, and virtually every other situation we face on a daily basis. For example, look at today's office. Fax machines, computers, portable cellular phones, and elaborate telephone systems were uncommon just a few years ago. Change is likely to accelerate at an even faster rate in the future.

You must continually "sell" the need for change to your staff, as well as accept it personally.

So much change creates a great challenge for supervisors. You must continually "sell" the need for change to your staff, as well as accept it personally.

Implementing Change

To implement change effectively, you should:

1. **Make a decision and stick to it.** Review the facts and whatever information you've collected and commit to the change you believe should be made.

2. **Develop a plan.** Decide on a plan to "sell" the new methods or new techniques to those staff who will be directly involved.

3. **Plan each phase of the change.** For example, in Chapter Three, Joan decided to shift a staff member from one department to another in the residential center. That change needs to be thought through with a plan to anticipate and cover each step.

   In our decision planner on pages 26-27, Joan would probably want to include the following.

- Explain to Jim the reasons for the change.
- Explain to Jim's new supervisor why the change is occurring.
- Have the new supervisor explain any new tasks Jim needs to learn.
- Explain to the other staff how the change will affect their jobs and discuss any future plans about staff.

4. **Examine possible alternatives to each step; draw up contingency plans.** Joan needs a contingency plan. Using the decision planner from Chapter Three, she would anticipate what would happen if Jim hated the new job. She might want to talk to her supervisor and see what other options would be open for Jim if the transfer doesn't work out. She could put Jim back in his original job and move Sally instead, or find some method to help them get along.

5. **Monitor staff behavior to ensure that the changes are implemented.** Here's an example:

   Don, the supervisor in the private corrections company, is regularly faced with a barrage of changes. One change that the company implements is a new compensation program that rewards employees for their productivity. At the same time, their base pay is reduced, with the potential for top staff to earn more.

   A likely outcome is that Don will find some staff excited about the new plan, others taking a wait-and-see attitude, and still others ready to sabotage the plan or quit their jobs. Their behavior and reactions will be Don's most visible clues.

The reality is that Don may lose some staff to frustration and a sense of loss. At the same time, other staff may become more valuable and more loyal.

The key for Don is to monitor his individual staff on how they are dealing with the change so that he can provide as much support as possible. This will help his staff deal positively with the change.

6. **Accept and plan for the results of change.** The new ideas and methods you implement may require work reassignments, changes in staff, or new tasks. As a supervisor, you should think of the possible outcomes and the likely results.

Take a Moment . . .

Think of a decision you are facing. Develop a change-implementation plan using the steps we've outlined.

1. **Make a decision.**
   Describe the decision you must make or have made.

   ____

   ____

   ____

   ____

   ____

   ____

2. **Describe your method of introducing and "selling" it to your staff.**
   See pages 42-43.

   ____

   ____

   ____

   ____

   ____

   ____

3. **Break your change down into smaller steps. We did this in our examples on pages 37-38.**

1. ________________	5. ________________
2. ________________	6. ________________
3. ________________	7. ________________
4. ________________	8. ________________

4. **Create a contingency plan.**

Possible Problem Result	Contingency Plan
______________________	______________________
______________________	______________________
______________________	______________________
______________________	______________________
______________________	______________________
______________________	______________________

5. **Monitor your staff's implementation of the change.** List the changes in behavior required and, under each behavior, list each person's response. Monitor behavior over the time period you've allowed for the change.

Behavior	Response
______________________	______________________
______________________	______________________
______________________	______________________
______________________	______________________
______________________	______________________
______________________	______________________

6. **Accept and plan for the results of change.** At the end of the acceptable break-in period, list the actions you plan to take for those who aren't meeting objectives.

____

____

____

____

____

Promoting the Need for Change

Source of Change
- **outside influences**
- **staff suggestions**

Being committed to a change and getting others to accept it are two different things. A planned change may result from outside influences, as in Don's situation. It may also result from you or one of your staff finding a better way to do things. In either case, you'll probably need to "sell" this change.

Steps to "Selling" Change to Your Staff

To "sell" a change to staff, follow these five steps.

Step One **Present the new idea to staff in clear, accessible language, both verbally and in writing.** Include the reasons for the change. It's much easier to get an idea accepted if people know why the change is occurring.

Step Two **Present your ideas in positive, sales-oriented language**, even if the change is likely to be resisted. Put it in the most positive light possible.

Step Three **As the new change is implemented, stress your willingness to help staff members adapt.** Be supportive as problems occur.

Step Four **If the change is a major one, ask each staff member to tell you how he or she plans to handle it on the job.** Let your staff know that you're personally interested in helping them.

Step Five **If the change has other unintended results, be open to reviewing what has occurred and to responding as needed.**

"Selling" Change to Your Supervisors

To "sell" your ideas for change to your supervisors, you'll need to follow Steps One and Two. As with the staff you supervise, present your ideas in clear, easy-to-understand language, both verbally and in writing. Use positive, sales-oriented language. After that, you must await your supervisor's decision.

. . . present your ideas in clear, easy-to-understand language, both verbally and in writing. Use positive, sales-oriented language.

To influence that decision, be prepared to provide additional supportive information and even to negotiate on some points of your new plan.

Don't be afraid to offer new ideas. Most managers welcome new methods and creativity on the part of their staff—especially supervisors.

Moving Forward

If you can answer "Yes" to the following questions, you have already started to understand how to implement change. If you are not able to answer "Yes" to these questions, it may be a good idea to reread this chapter on Managing Change.

1. Are you open to new ideas and change?
2. In your personal and work plans, do you list the factors that can affect your plans? Do you take into account external situations you can't control?

3. Do you develop contingency plans?
4. Do you take the time to "sell" the benefits of your ideas?
5. Do you plan ways to implement change with minimal disruption?

Chapter Four Review

1. True/False. Most people are risk-takers.
2. List at least four guidelines for implementing change effectively.

   ____

   ____

   ____

   ____

3. List the five steps to "selling" change to your staff.

   ____

   ____

   ____

   ____

   ____

4. Describe how to "sell" change to your supervisors.

   ____

   ____

   ____

   ____

   ____

Chapter Five

MANAGING YOUR TIME

Chapter Objectives

After completing this chapter, you should be able to:

- Identify your major time-wasters.
- Prioritize your work.
- Debunk some common myths that affect time management.

Do you find your workload overwhelming? Do you feel as if you're always behind on the projects you need to handle? Are things falling through the cracks and not getting done? Is your workday getting longer with no major improvement in results?

Losing control over your time creates these uncomfortable feelings. As a supervisor, you get tugged in all directions by people bringing what often seems like a never-ending stream of urgent problems.

What can you do? The first step is to determine that you want to control your time. Doing so will most likely involve delegating work to a greater degree (which we will discuss in Chapter Nine). But you can also take more time, now, to solve your time problems. You'll learn to carefully manage your long-term projects as well as address the day-to-day issues that come up.

Although this chapter will give you immediate tips on time management, consider reading more on the subject on your own afterward.

Identifying Major Time-Wasters

What are the most common time-wasters? The chart on the next page lists the most common time-wasters. Do any of these sound familiar?

Time-Wasters

Rate yourself on managing each time-waster, from *excellent* (give yourself a 1) to *average* (give yourself a 2) to *need help* (give yourself a 3).

Time-Waster	**Excellent** *(I don't do this.)*	**Average** *(I do this sometimes.)*	**Need Help** *(I do this frequently.)*
1. No priorities for my tasks	____	____	____
2. Doing too many things at once; leaving tasks unfinished	____	____	____
3. Too much attention to detail of other people's work	____	____	____
4. Too many meetings	____	____	____
5. Meetings run too long	____	____	____
6. Procrastination	____	____	____
7. Solving staff members' personal problems	____	____	____
8. Long phone conversations	____	____	____
9. Doing my staff's work	____	____	____
10. Unrealistic time estimates of projects	____	____	____
11. Poor scheduling	____	____	____
12. Poor communication with staff	____	____	____
13. Poor communication with supervisors	____	____	____
14. Too much paperwork with no clearly identified need	____	____	____
		Total	____

An ideal score is 14. A score of 22 or more indicates a need for improvement. A score of 28 or more means that you probably feel like you're drowning. You need to make a conscious decision to manage your time more effectively.

Prioritizing Your Work

Frequently, supervisors find they spend more time on projects they thought took little time (perhaps because the projects are more interesting, enjoyable, or easier) and actually very little time on projects that seem to be all-consuming (because the projects may be boring or difficult).

Not all projects and needs are equal. Part of your job as a supervisor is to make decisions (see Chapter Three) and determine which projects are most important and need your attention first. Before you can build a priority plan, however, you must know how you really spend your time.

Part of your job as a supervisor is to make decisions and determine which projects are most important and need your attention first.

In Chapter Three, we discussed the need for getting as much information as possible to make the best possible decision. The same advice holds true for time management. Doing a time log for a minimum of one week is essential, though two weeks of record-keeping will give you more accurate information.

Use the time log on page 48 for one workday. Record your activities for one workday in 15-minute increments as shown. Make 14 copies of this time log and track your time for two weeks. You may be surprised at how you really spend your time.

Note: If you work a different schedule, use the blank sheet on page 49 to write in the appropriate times.

Time Log

Task		Could Be Delegated?* Yes	No
7:00-7:15	______	☐	☐
7:15-7:30	______	☐	☐
7:30-7:45	______	☐	☐
7:45-8:00	______	☐	☐
8:00-8:15	______	☐	☐
8:15-8:30	______	☐	☐
8:30-8:45	______	☐	☐
8:45-9:00	______	☐	☐
9:00-9:15	______	☐	☐
9:15-9:30	______	☐	☐
9:30-9:45	______	☐	☐
9:45-10:00	______	☐	☐
10:00-10:15	______	☐	☐
10:15-10:30	______	☐	☐
10:30-10:45	______	☐	☐
10:45-11:00	______	☐	☐
11:00-11:15	______	☐	☐
11:15-11:30	______	☐	☐
11:30-11:45	______	☐	☐
11:45-12:00	______	☐	☐
Lunch	______	☐	☐
1:00-1:15	______	☐	☐
1:15-1:30	______	☐	☐
1:30-1:45	______	☐	☐
1:45-2:00	______	☐	☐
2:00-2:15	______	☐	☐
2:15-2:30	______	☐	☐
2:30-2:45	______	☐	☐
2:45-3:00	______	☐	☐
3:00-3:15	______	☐	☐
3:15-3:30	______	☐	☐
3:30-3:45	______	☐	☐
3:45-4:00	______	☐	☐
4:00-4:15	______	☐	☐
4:15-4:30	______	☐	☐
4:30-4:45	______	☐	☐
4:45-5:00	______	☐	☐

Time Log

Could Be Delegated?*

Task	Yes	No
______________________	☐	☐
______________________	☐	☐
______________________	☐	☐
______________________	☐	☐
______________________	☐	☐
______________________	☐	☐
______________________	☐	☐
______________________	☐	☐
______________________	☐	☐
______________________	☐	☐
______________________	☐	☐
______________________	☐	☐
______________________	☐	☐
______________________	☐	☐
______________________	☐	☐
______________________	☐	☐
______________________	☐	☐
______________________	☐	☐
______________________	☐	☐
______________________	☐	☐
______________________	☐	☐
______________________	☐	☐
______________________	☐	☐
______________________	☐	☐
______________________	☐	☐
______________________	☐	☐
______________________	☐	☐
______________________	☐	☐
______________________	☐	☐
______________________	☐	☐
______________________	☐	☐
______________________	☐	☐
______________________	☐	☐
______________________	☐	☐
______________________	☐	☐

*Be honest in your appraisal or evaluation. Don't worry about who else could handle the task yet, only whether it could be handled by someone else.

Creating Your Own Priority Plan

In the space provided on page 51, list all the activities that showed up on your time log. Next to each one, put:

"1" For an activity that you yourself must absolutely do.

"2" For an activity that you really should do.

"3" For an activity that you'd like to do but don't really need to do yourself.

Next to each task or activity, you should also list how much time per week you spend on it.

When you've completed the list, add up the time spent for number 1 tasks, number 2 tasks, and number 3 tasks. Then, assuming you work a 40-hour week, start eliminating number 3 tasks first, followed by number 2 tasks that put you over your available time. You can eliminate tasks through a combination of delegation (see Chapter Nine) and better management of each task in your number 1 and number 2 categories.

Priority Plan

Activity or Task	Priority *1 Must do* *2 Should do* *3 Don't have to do myself*	Time Spent Per Week

Number 1 Tasks ____

Number 2 Tasks ____

Eliminating Number 3 Tasks ____

Remaining Total of Time ____

Over 40

Yes ☐

No ☐

If "Yes," you need to eliminate tasks through:

- delegation
- better management of 1 and 2 tasks

Debunking Some Common Myths About Time Management

Myth 1: Being Busy Is Being Productive

Not if you're spending your time on number 3 priorities or fun tasks that don't really help you as a supervisor. Being busy has nothing to do with productivity. Maximizing how you use your time means a great deal more. It gives you more free time, or more time for creating new ideas.

New supervisors often find themselves highly efficient at their old jobs and far less efficient at being a supervisor.

Myth 2: Efficiency Is Effectiveness

Not necessarily. New supervisors often find themselves highly efficient at their old jobs and far less efficient at being a supervisor. It's more important to jump in with both feet and tackle the tasks of supervision than to continue to improve your efficiency in the old job.

Myth 3: An Open-Door Policy Works Best

There's no question that staff who have access to their supervisors on a regular basis are happier and more productive. Unfortunately, as a supervisor, you must place some limits on the use of your time. It is essential to preserve time for yourself to handle the supportive tasks of supervision as well as the face-to-face tasks. Consider specifying regular times when you're available and times when you're not to be disturbed (unless it's a true emergency).

. . . as a supervisor, you must place some limits on the use of your time.

Techniques to Manage Your Time

No matter what your log shows, there are some proven techniques you can use to better manage your time. They include:

- **Make weekly and daily to-do lists in order of priority.** Check off each task as it's completed, and you'll feel far more accomplished at the end of the day. You may want to use a priority system such as:

  A High Priority—Must do today

  B Medium Priority—Can do today or tomorrow

  C Low Priority—Can do sometime during the week

  Numbers work just as well. The key is for you to be comfortable using the system.

- **Plan what you're going to do at least one day ahead.** If you know what tasks await you tomorrow, organize tomorrow's to-do list today!
- **Plan telephone calls in advance.** By doing this, you know what you want to cover and can reduce your time on the phone.
- **Plan meetings—one-on-one or with a group—in advance.** If you call the meeting, take control of the agenda and stay on the subject.
- **Evaluate your time management several times during the day.** Take a look at how you're doing about a third of the way throughout your workday. Emergencies do come up and must be dealt with. Your priorities may change in these situations.
- **Look at your personal list of major time-wasters.** Develop an action plan to do something about your worst time-wasters.

Once you start to manage your time, you will be able to develop your abilities and take advantage of opportunities to help you achieve your goals.

In Conclusion

Do you want to achieve the same high levels of success as some of the most successful supervisors in the world? You must treat your own time as a precious resource to invest. Once you start to manage your time, you will be able to develop your abilities and take advantage of opportunities to help you achieve your goals.

Chapter Five Review

1. List six common time-wasters.

   ____

   ____

   ____

   ____

   ____

   ____

2. True/False. Two weeks is a good time frame for seeing how you spend your time.

3. True/False. Being busy ensures that you'll be productive.

4. True/False. Being an efficient supervisor will make you an effective supervisor as well.

5. List four techniques to better manage your time.

   ____

   ____

   ____

   ____

Chapter Six

COMMUNICATING EFFECTIVELY

Chapter Objectives

After completing this chapter, you should be able to:

- Explain how to listen effectively.
- Identify and define the meaning of body language commonly used in the United States.
- Explain how to get yourself heard.
- Use a checklist of good written communication.

Sandra is a supervisor in the training unit at a large county jail. She is younger and better educated than many of her staff and feels that she has great difficulty getting their support. They just don't seem to pay attention to her, and they complain that she really doesn't understand them or their needs. In her mind, there's a real "people problem," and she feels at a loss as how to solve it. Later in the chapter, we'll learn how Sandra can communicate more effectively with her staff.

The root of many communication problems is often a failure to use a common language.

"People Problems" Are Often "Communication Problems"

Problems like Sandra's are often communication problems. The root of many communication problems is often a failure to use a common language. Age, gender, education, cultural background, and a host of other factors can create communication gaps.

In any society, words and gestures often mean different things to different people. Understanding these differences is a valuable skill for a new supervisor. As a supervisor, you'll need to recognize such differences and develop a communication style that will help you reach each person.

How to Listen Effectively

Communication is always a two-way process. Someone says something, and someone else hears what was said. Because each person comes to the listening situation with a different background, there is often a gap between the speaker's intention and the listener's interpretation.

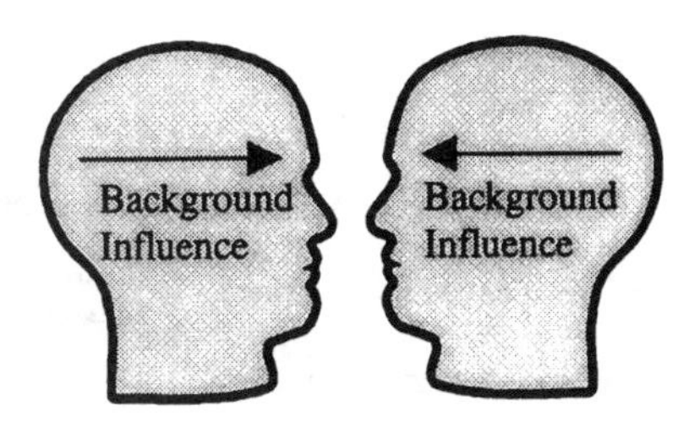

Ineffective listening can be a major communication problem. If you listen carefully, you'll have fewer people problems and more career success.

The Listening Process

The background and experience of each listener influences what is heard. If the experiences of speaker and listener are entirely different, there may be no communication.

Some years ago, an experiment with schoolchildren was carried out to analyze the kinds of words that were easiest to learn to spell. Conventional wisdom had always held that shorter words were easier to learn. The results showed, however, that nouns were easier to spell than adjectives, even though adjectives such as *this*, *blue*, and *big* were often shorter. Why? Nouns have tangible meaning, so people can picture them, thus making them easier to spell.

But there was a catch: nouns were easy to spell only if the nouns were familiar. For example, the word *cactus* was easy for students in the Southwest.

It was more difficult for students elsewhere who had never seen a cactus.

As a supervisor, you must be aware of your own background and prejudices, and eliminate them when you communicate with others.

Everybody understands concepts in the context of their own backgrounds. As a supervisor, you must be aware of your own background and prejudices, and eliminate them when you communicate with others. Prejudices are preconceived feelings or biases. The writer Voltaire called them opinions without judgment.

Take a Moment . . .

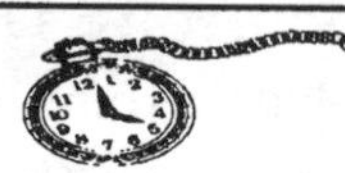

Think of someone with whom you have trouble communicating. Write down what you know about that person's background (age, gender, education, cultural background, etc.). Then, compare this information with your own background.

Individual

Age: ______________________

Gender: ______________________

Education: ______________________

Cultural Background: ______________

Other: ______________________

You

Age: ______________________

Gender: ______________________

Education: ______________________

Cultural Background: ______________

Other: ______________________

In what way do you think the differences in backgrounds are the source of your problem? ______________________

Seven Steps to Listening

Another problem we have with listening is that many of us think we're doing it, but we're not. We're actually hearing, not listening. *Hearing* is a physical act of processing sounds. However, *listening* is a blend of hearing and waiting, an intense connection with another person. Listening is an emotional and intellectual act that requires understanding what was said.

. . . *listening* is a blend of hearing and waiting, an intense connection with another person.

There are seven steps to effectively listening.

1. **Ask questions.** If something is unclear or seems to contradict what fits your own personal sense of logic, ask questions. Asking questions shows that you're interested in understanding what's being said.

2. **Concentrate.** Don't let your mind wander. People think at the rate of about 500 words per minute, but people talk at a rate of only about 150 words per minute. Stay focused on what is being said, or you risk missing key points.

3. **Listen for the main idea(s).** It's not uncommon for people to develop ideas as they talk, to be somewhat vague when discussing sensitive issues, or to have trouble coming to the point. Make sure that you determine what the person's key issues are. Restate the other person's main ideas in your own words and ask if you've understood correctly.

4. **Listen for the rationale behind what the other person is saying.** This is especially important if what he or she is saying doesn't seem to make sense to you. A staff member may be making a request on the

basis of erroneous information about the organization. Be sensitive and make sure that you understand why the person is saying what he or she is saying.

5. **Listen for key words.** Key words can become your own internal cue or memory stimulator to help you retain what you hear.

6. **Organize what you hear in your own mind in a way that is logical for you.** Your way of organizing information may differ from the way the information was presented, but it is critical for you to use what you hear.

7. **Take notes if the issue or request is complex.** It is worthwhile to get your thoughts down in writing.

Take a Moment . . .

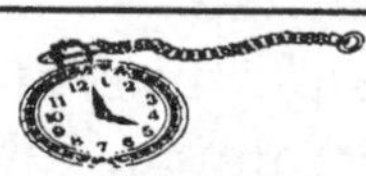

Think again about the person you described in the previous exercise. Which of the seven steps that we've just discussed might help you listen more effectively to that person?

- ___ **Ask questions.**
- ___ **Concentrate.**
- ___ **Listen for the main idea(s).**
- ___ **Listen for the rationale behind what the other person is saying.**
- ___ **Listen for key words.**
- ___ **Organize what you hear in your own mind in a way that is logical for you.**
- ___ **Take notes if the issue or request is complex.**

Try using the techniques you've selected the next time you talk with this person.

An Overview of Body Language

In addition to listening, communicating involves interpreting body language and getting your message heard.

Your verbal language conveys only part of what you mean. Body language—your gestures and movements—says the rest. The meanings of gestures and movements vary greatly from culture to culture. Here are just a few of the most common gestures in the United States and what they generally mean. Remember, in today's multicultural workforce, some of these gestures will have different meanings for those of different cultures. Check your library or bookstore for references on body language in various cultures.

The meanings of gestures and movements vary greatly from culture to culture.

- **Leaning forward is a positive gesture.** The person is listening carefully and wants to hear what is said.
- **Direct eye contact is a positive gesture.** Again, recognize this as a U.S. trait. Many Asian societies find direct eye contact quite rude.
- **Open hands are a sign of agreement and careful listening.**
- **Arms folded over the chest** is usually a very negative sign. Your words probably aren't getting through.
- **Leaning away** from you in a chair may indicate disinterest in what you are saying.
- **Backing away or avoidance** is generally a sign of disagreement or frustration with what you are saying.

Take a Moment . . .

Be aware of the gestures your staff and supervisors make as well as the signals you send with the same gestures.

Think once again about your face-to-face communication with the person in the previous exercises. What do you recall about that person's body language?

____

About your own body language?

____

What body language might you use to improve your communications with this person? ______________________

____

____

Make sure that your body language is a positive way to communicate with this person. If you are unsure about his or her culture, do a little research. Find out what is acceptable for that particular culture. Co-workers from the same culture and community groups are good resources.

Note: These same principles hold true for working with offenders.

How to Get Yourself Heard

How can you get yourself heard? Here are nine guidelines that can help get your message out.

1. **Present one idea at a time.** For example, if you're training staff in a new process, break

the process down into its most basic steps. Present each step separately and make sure that the step is understood before going on. If possible, provide an example or illustration of what you're trying to say to help overcome any built-in listening biases.

2. **Keep it simple.** Use basic language with common-use words. The English language is ambiguous enough without using slang, jargon, and industry buzz words.

3. **Make it brief.** Don't use more words or time than needed. Rather than clarify, highly detailed explanations may create confusion.

4. **Personalize what you're saying and present it to the individual.** Avoid generalizing or sounding vague. Add a personal touch.

5. **Use the right tone of voice and the right body language for the situation.** It seems obvious, but be aware of how you sound and look. Make sure that your voice and body language match the message you want to send. Sounding bored or looking disinterested tells the person you're talking to that what you're saying is not important—no matter what your words are saying.

6. **Get acceptance of each idea you present.** Make sure that the person understands you. If the person looks confused or doesn't question your ideas, he or she may not clearly understand what you said. Ask whether anything needs to be cleared up before you go on to your next point.

7. **Respond to the emotions of the people with whom you're talking.** Often, the subject will generate strong feelings. "Listen" carefully to other people's body language and to what they say.

8. **Appreciate your listeners' concerns.** Your listeners may disagree with you, in which case it's important to find out the basis of that disagreement. You don't have to back down from your position, just be sensitive to your listeners' reactions.

9. **Encourage your listeners to express themselves.** Welcome their thoughts and ideas so that you'll know how they're reacting. Again, you don't have to agree, but it's important for you to know what others are thinking.

Take a Moment . . .

Think about the last time you spoke to a group of your staff. Which of the nine steps on pages 62-64 did you use?

- ☐ **Present one idea at a time.**
- ☐ **Keep it simple.**
- ☐ **Make it brief.**
- ☐ **Personalize what you're saying and present it to the individual.**
- ☐ **Use the right tone of voice and the right body language for the situation.**
- ☐ **Get acceptance of each idea you present.**
- ☐ **Respond to the emotions of the people with whom you're talking.**
- ☐ **Appreciate your listeners' concerns.**
- ☐ **Encourage your listeners to express themselves.**

Plan your next communication with a group of your staff. Which of the nine steps will be particularly helpful to you?

____

____

Effective Writing

Read the memo on page 65 from Sandra to her staff in the training unit, then answer the questions that follow. The questions make up a checklist of the basics of good written communication.

MEMO

To: All Training Unit Staff
From: Sandra
Re: Your Good Ideas Can Mean More Time Off

Our organization is launching a new suggestion award program that is open to all staff.

Based on the idea that you know better than anyone else (including supervisors and managers) what we do well and where we need to improve, the organization is offering a reward of time off for every good suggestion made to improve the way we do things.

Submit each suggestion to me on the attached form (I have more copies of the form if you need them). I will pass all suggestions on to our suggestion review committee. The committee consists of one frontline staff member and one supervisor from each department.

The committee will evaluate your suggestion, and you will earn an award based on what we feel your suggestion will contribute to the jail's well-being. An award schedule is also attached.

Please review the following documents and call or see me if you have any questions.

Checklist for Good Written Communication

Answer these questions about Sandra's memo.

- ☐ Does it command the reader's attention?
- ☐ Does it generate interest in the reader?
- ☐ Does it get the reader involved?
- ☐ Does it get the reader to take action (promising a benefit, providing proof of the need for something, communicating a sense of urgency, etc.)?
- ☐ Is it reader-oriented rather than writer-oriented?
- ☐ Is it clear and concise?
- ☐ Is it tactful and courteous (no threatening language)?
- ☐ Is the tone conversational and the English simple?
- ☐ Is the information useful to the reader?
- ☐ Is it likely to produce the desired affect on the reader?

When you put something in writing, compare it to this checklist to make sure that it sends the message you want to send. If not, revise your communication to clarify your message and make it more effective.

Take a Moment . . .

Write a memo to your staff about a subject that should be put in writing.

MEMO

To: ____________________
From: ____________________
Date: ____________________
Subject: ____________________

Take a Moment *(continued)*

Now use the checklist to evaluate your memo.

- ☐ Does it command the reader's attention?
- ☐ Does it generate interest in the reader?
- ☐ Does it get the reader involved?
- ☐ Does it get the reader to take action (promising a benefit, providing proof of the need for something, communicating a sense of urgency, etc.)?
- ☐ Is it reader-oriented rather than writer-oriented?
- ☐ Is it clear and concise?
- ☐ Is it tactful and courteous (no threatening language)?
- ☐ Is the tone conversational and the English simple?
- ☐ Is the information useful to the reader?
- ☐ Is it likely to produce the desired affect on the reader?

Does your memo meet all of the guidelines? If not, go back and revise your memo. If you're unsure about one of the guidelines, ask a fellow supervisor or your supervisor to review it. An "outside" or "unbiased" review is often helpful.

In Conclusion

A management expert once said, "Most supervision problems are communication problems," which proves the importance of communication skills, both verbal and written, for supervisors.

Basic communication is a skill that many new supervisors overlook, and a skill that veteran supervisors must re-strengthen regularly. A technique for becoming a better communicator is to become acutely aware of your own background and prejudices and eliminate them. By doing this, you will be able to communicate more effectively with your staff and peers.

A technique for becoming a better communicator is to become acutely aware of your own background and prejudices and eliminate them.

Chapter Six Review

1. The ________ and _______ of each listener influences what is heard.

2. Describe the difference between hearing and listening.

   ____

   ____

   ____

   ____

3. List the seven steps for effective listening.

   ____

   ____

   ____

   ____

   ____

   ____

   ____

4. Identify three positive and three negative gestures or body movements commonly used in the United States.

____

____

____

____

____

____

5. List five guidelines for getting yourself heard.

____

____

____

____

____

6. Using key words, identify three guidelines for effective writing.

____

____

____

For example:

commands the reader's attention
generates reader's interest
involves the reader

Chapter Seven

MAKING MEETINGS PRODUCTIVE

Chapter Objectives

After completing this chapter, you should be able to:

- Explain how to prepare for one-on-one meetings with a staff member or manager.
- Describe how to prepare for your own meeting with a group.
- Describe how to address typical meeting problems.

Omar was recently promoted to quality control supervisor for prison industries. He has participated in meetings on quality, customer care, and office procedures, and, of course, he has had one-to-one conferences with his supervisor. Now there seems to be a never-ending stream of meetings with his staff, fellow supervisors, people from other departments, customers, and suppliers. Moreover, he's often the one leading meetings, which means he has to create the agenda. Later in the chapter, we will learn how Omar can lead productive meetings.

One-on-One Meetings

As a supervisor, the one-on-one meeting is the most common type you will experience. You might meet with someone on your staff, your supervisor, other supervisors, or offenders.

Maximizing Your Meeting Time Preparation

If you are the one who is responsible for the meeting, you should ensure that it is effective. Start by rereading Chapters Five and Six on time management and effective communication. Then ask yourself the following questions. Don't begin your meeting until you have the answers.

1. What is the purpose of this meeting?
2. How long should it take?
3. What am I going to say and in what order?
4. What is the outcome I want? What am I expecting the other person to do?
5. How is/are the person(s) likely to react to what I'm going to say?
6. What other topics are likely to come up, and am I prepared for them?
7. How will I end the meeting?

Note: These questions also apply to other meetings for which you are responsible, such as staff meetings. Before going into your next one-on-one meeting, you may want to complete the following form.

One-on-One Meeting Preparation Form

Meeting with ____________________

Purpose(s) ____________________

____

____

Desired length ____________________

Key points I'm going to make

1. ____________________

2. ____________________

3. ____________________

4. ____________________

Desired results ____________________

____

____

Likely Response	My Reply
____________	____________
____________	____________

Possible topics that may come up ____________________

____

End meeting by ____________________

Action to be taken:

By me ____________________

____

By others ____________________

____

Documentation required ____________________

Leading a Meeting with Your Group

Supervisor-led meetings are a mainstay of organizations. They cover everything from presenting policy to hearing staff problems, from developing quality techniques to reviewing procedures.

Have you ever sat through meetings that were boring, that didn't affect you, or that you didn't care about? If you did, you are not alone. By following the rules below, you can avoid these problems and make your meetings better.

1. **Avoid a meeting, if possible.** Rule 1 is not a contradiction. If you can convey the same information by memo or on the phone with each person, it will probably be faster. Meetings are one of the biggest time-wasters today. Indeed, you may have indicated meetings as one of your top five time-wasters in Chapter Five.

2. **Keep the group small.** Smaller groups tend to work more effectively and rapidly. You'll often get more interaction as well because people usually are more willing to speak up in smaller groups.

   If your group will be voting on issues, have an odd number of people to avoid ties.

3. **Give everyone an agenda in advance.** Tell everyone what will be covered, and let them know that only items on the agenda will be discussed. If you want to allow people to add their own ideas, that's fine but, again, the complete agenda should go out to everyone in advance.

   Word your agenda carefully to describe the

issues in broad terms without imposing a decision. For example, suppose Omar, our quality control supervisor, were to include on a staff meeting agenda, "Improving the production techniques to stay on schedule." What kind of reaction would he get? Omar is assuming that the production techniques are a problem when, in fact, other issues may pose problems as well. Omar will have limited everyone to talking about the production techniques, when they may not be the cause of the problem.

4. **Invite only those people who really need to attend.** Sometimes protocol requires inviting certain people, but, if possible, stick with Rule 2—keep the group small.

5. **Start on time and end as soon as you've covered the agenda.** Don't delay your starting time. Attendees should be ready when the meeting is scheduled. Also, don't get into other subject areas.

6. **Keep the discussion focused.** Don't let participants get off on tangents or other issues. Save those for future meetings. One way to bring the discussion back to where you want it is to ask a question related to the subject.

7. **When someone suggests an idea, write it down and repeat it with slightly different phrasing.** The objective is to get the whole group involved with the idea, not just the individual who presented it.

8. **If someone criticizes someone else in the group, jump in immediately and**

rephrase his or her comment in a more positive way. You don't want your meeting to become a personal gripe session. For example, if Marta complains, "Carlos, you're so inexperienced that you can't see beyond the problems with the production techniques!" Omar might rephrase and redirect the comment by saying, "Marta thinks we may have other problems besides the production techniques. What other problems do we have?"

9. **Draw in everyone.** Assuming that everyone has a reason to be there, ask questions or opinions from the silent attendees. Make them a part of the discussion.

10. **Don't be afraid of heated discussion or disagreement—as long as it doesn't involve personal attacks.** You want to encourage people to express what they're thinking. Doing so may lead to new ideas.

11. **Remain calm and neutral, whatever happens.** Your role as a supervisor is to moderate and facilitate, not to take sides or discourage comments.

12. **Summarize what was accomplished in the meeting and state what action needs to be taken and by whom.** Let everyone know what they achieved during the meeting and what follow up, if any, must be done. If you gave out assignments, repeat them in specific, clear language to the individuals and restate the deadlines for completing the assignments.

Follow these 12 rules, and you're on your way to leading productive meetings that are worth the time and effort of everyone involved.

Take a Moment . . .

Think about the last meeting you had, or pick one that you recently attended. Which of the 12 steps might have improved the meeting and why?

- ☐ Avoid a meeting, if possible. ____________________
- ☐ Keep the group small. ____________________
- ☐ Give everyone an agenda in advance. ____________________
- ☐ Invite only those people who really need to attend.

  ____
- ☐ Start on time and end as soon as you've covered the agenda.

  ____
- ☐ Keep the discussion focused. ____________________
- ☐ When someone suggests an idea, write it down and repeat it with slightly different phrasing. ____________________

  ____
- ☐ If someone criticizes someone else in the group, jump in immediately and rephrase his or her comment in a more positive way.

  ____
- ☐ Draw in everyone. ____________________
- ☐ Don't be afraid of heated discussion or disagreement—as long as it doesn't involve personal attacks. ____________________

  ____
- ☐ Remain calm and neutral, whatever happens. ____________________

  ____
- ☐ Summarize what was accomplished in the meeting and state what action needs to be taken and by whom. ____________________

Typical Meeting Problems

When you're running a meeting, it's up to you to keep the meeting on track. You need to deal quickly with problems that arise so they won't derail your meeting. Most typical meeting problems can be handled simply and effectively, as outlined in the following tips.

Problem	Response
One or two people dominate the discussion.	Set a time limit on each response.
One or two won't talk.	Ask attendees for an opinion.
People are losing interest.	Ask someone in the group for a specific example or move to another subject.
Discussion drifts off the subject.	Ask questions to get attendees back on the topic.
An argument develops.	Remind the group that it's okay for people to have different opinions, and encourage everyone to hear all points of view
You make an obvious mistake.	Admit it and joke about it—supervisors aren't expected to be perfect.

The outcomes of meetings are greatly influenced by how you manage the meetings. If you follow the 12 steps and move quickly to handle typical problems, you'll get better results from the meetings.

When Someone Else Calls the Meeting

If someone else calls the meeting, you cannot do much to control the agenda, but you certainly can take steps to be as prepared as possible.

Preparing may include researching information that your supervisor might request, creating a report, or being aware of a particular situation.

If someone on your staff asks to hold a meeting, you should take similar steps. You do retain the right to control the agenda or deny the request for a meeting if you think the staff member's agenda is inappropriate. If you deny the request, offer the staff member a chance to meet with you out of courtesy. Be sure to allow the person to present his or her thoughts and ideas openly. The flow of accurate information is critical to you, your supervisor, and your staff. You should do nothing to discourage people from being open and honest with you.

Moving Forward

If you can answer "Yes" to the following questions, you already have started to understand how to make meetings more productive. If you are not able to answer "Yes" to these questions, reread this chapter on Making Meetings Productive.

For one-on-one meetings that you set up, do you:

- Think in advance about what you're going to say and how you will say it?
- Anticipate how you might reply to the other person's response?

For group meetings that you run, do you:

- Prepare in advance, involve everyone, and provide an open environment for discussion?
- Summarize the results and clarify any follow-up needed?

For meetings called by others, do you:

- Think about what information you'll need to prepare?
- Ask in advance what the purpose of the meeting is?

Chapter Seven Review

1. Identify the seven questions you should ask yourself before beginning a meeting.

____

____

____

____

____

____

____

2. The 12 rules for conducting a productive meeting are:

- Avoid a ______________, if possible.
- Keep the group ______________.
- Give everyone an ____________ in advance.
- Invite only those people who ___________ to attend.
- Start and end as soon as your_________ has been covered.
- Keep the discussion ___________ .
- Write down ideas and ________ them with slightly ________ phrasing.
- If someone criticizes another, jump in ________ and rephrase the comment in a __________ way.
- ______ ______ everyone.
- Don't be afraid of _____________ __________ or __________ .
- Remain _____ and _________, no matter what happens.
- Summarize _________________ and clarify _______________ .

3. How do you deal with each of the situations so that your meeting runs smoothly?

   A. You hold a meeting to resolve problems relating to transporting offenders. But the topic drifts toward problems in a certain cellblock.

   ____

   B. You're conducting a meeting and two of your staff are dominating the discussion.

   ____

   C. During a meeting, you accidentally call a new staff member by the wrong name.

   ____

   D. Smith and Johnson are not participating in the discussion. They're just sitting and listening to what is being said.

   ____

   E. You notice during a meeting that staff appear to be getting bored—you see tapping pens, eyes glaring at watches, eyes staring off into space, and bodies slumping in chairs.

   ____

   F. In the middle of your meeting, Randall and Vickers start arguing with each other over a point.

   ____

4. If someone else calls a meeting, you should:

   ____A. Do nothing but attend.
   ____B. Write down and submit ideas for the agenda.
   ____C. Critique the agenda and return it before the meeting.
   ____D. Be prepared for the meeting.

Chapter Eight

PRAISE, CRITICISM, AND CONFLICT

Chapter Objectives

After completing this chapter, you should be able to:

- Explain how and when praise should be used.
- Explain how and when criticism should be used.
- Describe how to manage staff conflicts.

Kelly recently started as a nursing supervisor at a large prison hospital. Her predecessor left several months prior to her arrival, and the staff has been reporting directly to her supervisor. Because there has been no direct supervision for several months, Kelly is finding it necessary to talk to her staff and get things in shape. Some of them have been doing a great job, while others have been performing well below acceptable levels. A number of unresolved conflicts also remain. Kelly will need to use a combination of praise, criticism, and conflict-resolution skills.

Praise . . . ranks very high on the list of what people want from their jobs.

Using Praise

Praise is a powerful tool for any supervisor. As you recall from Chapter Two, it ranks very high on the list of what people want from their jobs. Your staff wants to be recognized when they do something well or something beyond their basic responsibilities. This recognition reaffirms their own self-worth and increases their confidence in doing a good job.

Here are some basic tips for using praise:

- **Mean what you say.** Make it sincere. Don't exaggerate or say things you really don't mean. This diminishes the affect of the praise.
- **Say what you mean.** Don't "pile it on." Be specific and avoid generalities like "great job." Kelly's staff would rather hear, "You did an excellent job of handling the rush of patients we had today."
- **Balance your use.** Praise, while a great form of recognition, will lose most of its affect if it becomes regular and predictable. Save it for when it's deserved.
- **Use praise to provide encouragement.** If you ask some of your staff to take on a new assignment, use praise:

  • to express your confidence in them to get the job done. This early praise will help your staff get off to a good start.

  • while they're doing the assignment. This praise will give them the confidence to complete the job successfully.

When Is the Best Time to Praise People?

Praise offered soon after a task has great influence . . .

The best time is right after they've completed a task or when they're ready to take on new and challenging work.

Praise offered soon after a task has great influence for several reasons:

- The task is fresh in the mind of your staff member.

- You demonstrated your interest in what he or she was doing soon after the task was completed.
- It reinforces self-confidence.

Praise can be offered publicly or privately. Naturally, if the praise is truly genuine, most people like the public recognition that goes with the honor of doing a good job. If you praise in public, however, do it uniformly so that none of your staff feel left out of the picture. A word of caution: Be sure to assess your environment before deciding to praise a staff member in public. If it will embarrass the staff member or subject him or her to ridicule, give the praise in private.

Using Criticism

For most supervisors, criticism is far more difficult to handle than praise. You don't want to hurt anyone's feelings, and you're always concerned about how the staff member might react.

Take a Moment . . .

Examine a current problem you're having with a staff member. Fill in the chart below to prepare for applying the techniques that follow.

Staff name: ____________________

Title: ____________________

Description of the problem. Describe only the work- related problem—don't mention personality issues or reasons for it:

____

____

____

____

Possible causes; list all possible causes:

____

____

____

Take A Moment *(continued)*

Key points to correct the problem:

___

___

___

Keys to Effective Criticism

When you must criticize a staff member, follow these guidelines to be effective.

- **Limit your comments to the behavior.** Don't label people as stubborn, difficult, or easygoing. Don't criticize the person; focus on the task. Kelly, our nursing supervisor, would be far better off telling a staff member that a specific report was late and letting him or her respond—rather than berating the staff member for tardiness in general.
- **Criticize as quickly as possible when you discover a problem.** The problem is fresh in the mind of the staff member, so you'll generally get a more accurate response.
- **Listen carefully to what the staff member has to say.** Get the staff member's opinion; let the staff member tell you what went wrong. Ask what he or she thinks the problem is. Don't prejudge an answer. Keep an open mind to what you hear.
- **Be considerate.** Get your point across without being rude, curt, or loud. Losing your temper may put the other person on the defensive and probably won't help you solve the problem or determine its cause.
- **Don't present criticism with praise.** It sends a confusing message. There's often a tendency to want to say something nice to soften the blow. It doesn't work! It may blunt the criticism, but the praise means nothing. The staff member hears only the bad news.
- **Don't trap or humiliate staff members.** For example, assume that

the prison hospital where Kelly works receives a complaint letter from a doctor identifying a difficult nurse. Suppose that Kelly asks the nurse if he or she had a problem with a doctor, and then traps the nurse by discussing the complaint. That would be a mistake. Kelly should be straightforward in talking with the nurse about the problem.

Take a Moment . . .

Use the keys to effective criticism and make notes outlining the conversation you plan to have with your staff member about the problem you described on page 84.

How will you focus on behavior?

____

____

How will you pinpoint the earliest time to talk with the staff member? ______________________________

____

____

How will you listen carefully to what the staff member has to say?

____

____

How will you be considerate? ______________________________

____

____

How will you present the criticism without citing any praise?

____

____

How will you avoid trapping the staff member? ______________

____

What Is The Best Time and Place to Criticize?

Depending on how severe the problem is, choose your office or workstation, the staff member's office or workstation, or neutral ground (such as a cafeteria, extra office, or lobby). If the problem is severe, the individual should come to you. It demonstrates just how serious the problem is. For a less formal and less intimidating mood, choose the staff member's location or a neutral site. Doing so sends a far less severe message than when you call the staff member to your location. Regardless of the site, however, be sure to give the criticism in private—where no one else can hear your conversation, be it a staff member or an offender.

Regardless of the site, be sure to give the criticism in private . . .

Choose a time that's conducive to solving the problem as well. Don't deliver bad news (like criticism) just as the person is taking on some new task or project. It's also wise to avoid doing it over lunch or late in the day.

Generally, the best time for criticism is early in the day. This way, the staff member can get on with his or her job and cool off by the end of the day.

Written Criticism

Think carefully before you decide to prepare written criticism. The outcome may be more negative than productive. In many cases, your best bet is to express criticism verbally because written criticism may have unintended consequences:

- Written criticism is far more severe than verbal criticism.

- It becomes part of the staff member's record, which could affect promotions and layoffs.
- The staff member may not have an opportunity to respond to or explain what occurred.
- The criticism remains an issue for a long time.
- Your comments may lack clear meaning because your tone of voice or any further explanation is not available to the reader.

Managing Conflicts

Conflicts between your staff will occur. Many of them may seem unimportant in the larger scheme of the organization, but they cannot be treated that way.

Judge the issues, not the personalities.

Practice the same techniques you would with criticism and praise. Listen carefully to each person involved. Judge the issues, not the personalities. Don't generalize or assume that the less competent or more "troublesome" person is the cause of the conflict. After hearing the issues, make your decision (review Chapter Three on decision making) and handle any criticisms in the manner described in this chapter.

The Five Steps to Successful Conflict Management

The conflict management process involves five steps. Following these steps carefully will help you solve conflicts more effectively.

1. **Take responsibility for dealing with conflict.** Taking the initiative to intervene in a conflict situation has much greater poten-

tial for making matters better—for turning what may have looked like a hopeless lose-lose situation into a win-win opportunity.

You can't turn a conflict into a win-win opportunity unless you first make the decision to take personal responsibility for dealing with conflict.

2. **Uncover, define, and discuss the real problem.** When defining the conflict, cast yourself in the role of a detective who needs to check, double-check, and triple-check every shred of evidence. Your task at this point isn't to find a solution. It's to simply uncover and accurately define the problem. Once you define the problem, set ground rules and discuss the problem. Don't keep emotions out of the discussion. Let it out!

   Expressing true emotions doesn't mean that your meeting needs to become a shouting match. There are ways to promote totally open communication with no holding back and to do it in a controlled and productive way. You just have to establish the ground rules, which are:

   - Everyone will be open and honest.
   - Everyone will have a say and be heard.
   - Everyone will listen to each other without argument or negative reaction and will keep a positive, caring attitude.
   - Opinions and feelings must be supported by facts or examples of specific behavior.

3. **Ask questions and listen!** Listed below are valuable tips for asking questions and lis-

tening effectively. When you follow these tips, you'll also send the message that you're actually interested in what people have to say.

Asking the Right Question:

- Ask open-ended questions (they require more than a "Yes" or "No" response) that prompt thoughtful, informative answers.
- Choose your words carefully so that they're a true reflection of the kind of response you're looking for.
- Follow up with targeted probing questions if an initial answer misses the mark or doesn't go into as much detail as you'd like.

Positive things can happen when you show people that you're listening actively and objectively.

Successful Listening Tips

- Listen objectively and with an open mind.
- Reassure the other person that you're interested in his or her perception of the situation.
- Offer positive feedback by paraphrasing (repeating in your own words) what you've heard and following up with questions based on the new information.

Positive things can happen when you show people that you're listening actively and objectively. Your feedback tells them that you understand their problems. When that happens, you'll find that, like you, they will begin to take personal responsibility for working toward a solution to the problem!

4. **Set goals and create an action plan.** Set goals and create an action plan together with those involved in the conflict. This will help you gain commitment from the others and ensure that everyone understands the plan.

   Finally, don't let the meeting end until you've found out if its communication has been successful. Ask if everyone agrees on the problem that has been defined. Ask for everyone's honest commitment. If you sense that it's not entirely there, open up the meeting to more discussion.

5. **Follow up.** Now it's time to create a follow-up plan to make sure that the initial conflict does not arise at a later date. Be sure to include a date and time for a follow-up meeting to go over progress and make sure that people are still on track.

   The responsibility and sincerity you show throughout the conflict management process will reward you and your organization with improved communication, morale, and productivity.

. . . give praise when it's deserved, give criticism in private soon after the situation occurs, and take responsibility for dealing with conflict.

In Conclusion

Giving praise and criticism, and managing conflict are an essential part of your job. Following the guidelines presented in this chapter will help you carry out these responsibilities effectively. Remember to give praise when it's deserved, give criticism in private soon after the situation occurs, and take responsibility for dealing with conflict.

Chapter Eight Review

1. Identify four tips for giving praise.

 ____

 ____

 ____

 ____

2. True/False. You should praise staff soon after they complete a task.
3. List three guidelines for giving effective criticism.

 ____

 ____

 ____

4. True/False. You always should criticize a staff member in front of other staff.
5. True/False. In most cases, it is better to use written criticism rather than verbal criticism so that the staff member can remember the issues involved.
6. List the five steps for managing conflicts.

 ____

 ____

 ____

 ____

 ____

7. Asking the right questions means:
   - Asking _______ questions
   - Choosing your _______ carefully
   - Following up with _______ _______ _______ if the initial answer is not sufficient
8. Listening successfully means:
   - Listen _______ and with an _______ mind
   - Reassure the other person that you're interested in his or her _______ of the situation
   - Offer _______ _______ by _______ what you've heard and following up with questions based on the new information

Chapter Nine

DELEGATING WORK

Chapter Objectives

After completing this chapter, you should be able to:

- Describe the process of delegating work.
- Identify the types of tasks that should be delegated.
- Create a plan to make delegation work for you.

Rose was recently promoted to supervisor in the regional probation office, where she's worked for the past four years as an agent. As a probation officer, Rose was very competent and consistently worked successfully with clients. She is reluctant to give up her clients, with whom she has developed a strong working relationship.

She's finding the supervision aspects of her job to be very time-consuming (filing reports, helping other officers and teaching them, attending meetings). Rose is still trying to take care of some of her old clients. In fact, she is doing some of the work her staff should be doing because they don't seem to do it properly. "It just seems better to do it myself, but there isn't enough time in the day to manage it all," says Rose.

Why Must Supervisors Delegate Work?

One answer is obvious, as Rose found out; there isn't enough time in the day to do everything. There are other reasons as well:

- **Delegating work to others improves your time management and productivity.** As you recall from Chapter Five, one of the keys to successful time management is to eliminate tasks that others can do.
- **Delegating work is more efficient.** Supervising is a full-time job in most organizations. Your role, as discussed in Chapter One, is to supervise the activities of others. You and your staff doing your proper jobs is more efficient for the organization as a whole.
- **Delegating work develops the skills and abilities of others.** Doing the work yourself often seems faster and easier because your staff may have not yet learned the tasks as well as you have. They never will, if you don't give them a chance. Valuable, efficient staff will make you look good as well.
- **Delegation increases job satisfaction for your staff.** It shows that you're interested in developing their skills and trusting them with responsibility.
- **It helps you better evaluate your staff.** If you're always stepping in, you can't be a fair judge of others' work. After all, they have not had a chance to prove themselves. As a supervisor, you're far better off supporting your staff's efforts and helping them rather than taking over tasks yourself.

Why Avoid Delegation?

With so many good reasons for delegating work, why are some supervisors reluctant to do it?

Check off the reasons that make you hesitate to delegate work:

- ☐ **Less power and influence.** Did you derive a sense of power and influence from your work prior to being a supervisor? If so, it's quite easy to feel a sense of loss when someone else is doing the task. For many, giving up a task feels like taking away some of their own self-worth.
- ☐ **Less control over the job.** Someone else is now in control of the task. As a supervisor, you can find it frustrating to know that your staff are doing what you used to do and maybe learning to do it better.
- ☐ **Giving up the "fun" stuff.** Every job has favorite elements for every staff member. Perhaps Rose truly enjoyed meeting and talking with new clients and now rarely gets to do that as a supervisor. She feels frustrated when she sees other people doing what she enjoyed so much. Perhaps when she sees others doing things differently, she sometimes thinks they're not doing things as well as she used to.

Take a Moment . . .

What are some of the other reasons why you may be reluctant to delegate work?

____

____

____

____

____

____

The Process of Delegation

Delegation begins with understanding the goal of your job and the jobs of the people who work for you. If there is no written description for their positions, take the time to write one. Doing so can help both you and your staff focus on what you're all trying to accomplish.

Delegation begins with understanding the goal of your job and the jobs of the people who work for you.

Once that is done, create a list of the tasks for which people are currently responsible. In the probation agency, the list might include meeting with clients, asking questions, answering questions, offering ideas, and following up with clients' employers.

Set goals for each of your staff for the tasks they must handle. Let your staff know what you expect of them. At the same time, be sensitive to their needs. Make sure that they understand what you're asking of them and what they'll have to do. If they're not sure what task needs to be done or how to do it, it will be difficult for them to meet the goal. When you delegate a task for the first time, it's especially critical to communicate clearly.

It's also critical to supervise your staff members' performance and make sure that they learn to do the tasks correctly. Remember, part of your job as a supervisor is to foster your staff's development. The more skills your staff learn, the more productive they become, and the more efficient your unit or department runs.

What Types of Tasks Can Be Delegated?

You can't delegate your entire job away, so what should you delegate?

1. **Start by listing all of your own tasks.** If necessary, keep a time log for several weeks to see what you do on a daily basis. You may want to use the log you started in Chapter Five on page 48. Then identify those tasks suitable for delegation. Some tasks, such as performance evaluations, cannot be delegated. Start your list here:

2. **Identify the most routine tasks.** These are the day-to-day things that could easily be learned and handled by someone else. Note your most routine tasks here:

3. **Get rid of the trivial tasks.** These tasks are not worth your time as a supervisor. Again, be objective. Don't hang onto trivial tasks that are fun or easy. Your time as a supervisor is too valuable to waste on these. Note the trivial tasks here: ______________________________

____

____

____

____

____

4. **Give up the time-consuming tasks that others could handle.** Even if the task is one you truly enjoy, you cannot afford to spend a lot of time on it as a supervisor. Note time-consuming tasks that others could handle here: ______________________________

____

____

____

____

____

____

5. **Look for parts of your job that could be easily taught to others.** What do you do that could be handled by others with just a little instruction? Note easy-to-teach tasks here: ______________________

____

____

____

____

____

____

____

Creating a Delegation Plan

Once you've decided to delegate work, here are three key rules to follow.

- **Don't take an assignment back after you've delegated it.** Help the person learn how to do it and be patient, but don't take over for him or her. Doing so demoralizes the conscientious worker who is really trying and gives the lazy worker a perfect way out: "Do a bad job, and let the supervisor take it over for you."
- **Encourage your staff to learn and make their own decisions about how to do the task.** Be patient, but at the same time, insist that the task be done correctly.
- **Make sure that you've clearly defined what you want your staff to do.** And make sure that they understand what you expect. Ideally, you'll be able to involve them in setting the objectives for the task.

Now it's time to delegate. Below is a plan to help you delegate your work.

A Plan for Delegating Work

1. Make a list of the tasks you're responsible for doing.
2. Create a time log for each task.
3. By staff member, list the skills and talents your various staff have. What do they do well?
4. Place the name of a staff member next to each task from item 1.
5. Write instructions for the task.

6. Have a backup plan in case staff are truly unable to do the task.
7. Periodically, review the tasks that have been delegated to see how people are doing.

Sample Chart

For example, Rose at the probation office would start by making a list of her own tasks to delegate and the skills and talents of each staff member. She would then set up the chart as shown.

	Employees			
	Sue	**Don**	**Mary**	**Kim**
Rose's Tasks				
Answer phone	1		2	
Greet new clients		1		2
Check messages	1		2	
Organize files			2	1

1 is her first delegation choice; 2 is her second choice.

In Conclusion

Now it's your turn. List the tasks you're responsible for performing. Refer to your time log and previous exercises if necessary.

My Tasks

____

____

____

____

____

____

List the names of your staff and write a brief description of their talents. For example, a staff member with excellent report writing skills can help prepare some of the reports you need that you don't have time to do yourself.

Name	Special Skills
______________	______________
______________	______________
______________	______________
______________	______________

Below, list down the left side of the chart the tasks you do that can be delegated. List the staff members' names across the top of the chart. Put a star or 1 in each space where the person is best-suited to do the job. Put a 2 next to your backup person, if you can identify one.

MyTask	**Staff Member/Suitability Rating**		
	_____	_____	_____
______________	_____	_____	_____
______________	_____	_____	_____
______________	_____	_____	_____
______________	_____	_____	_____
______________	_____	_____	_____
______________	_____	_____	_____
______________	_____	_____	_____
______________	_____	_____	_____

You now have the tools to properly delegate your work. Now do it! Remember to follow up to ensure that tasks are being done properly.

Chapter Nine Review

1. Identify three benefits of delegating tasks to staff.

 ____

 ____

 ____

2. Identify three reasons why supervisors are reluctant to delegate tasks to staff.

 ____

 ____

 ____

3. True/False. You can delegate any of your tasks to staff.
4. List the three key rules for delegating work to staff.

 ____

 ____

 ____

Chapter Ten

THE COMPLETE SUPERVISOR

Chapter Objectives

After completing this chapter, you should be able to:

- Describe how to examine your staff's needs.
- Describe what your organization expects of you as a supervisor.
- Explain how to evaluate and improve your supervisory skills in the future.

What do your staff members really want? What motivates them to follow your leadership and your direction? What does the organization want? What can or should you be doing to improve your own skills to be a better supervisor?

Knowing the answers to these questions will help you become the complete supervisor.

Surveys often have shown a disparity between what people want out of a job and what their supervisors think they want.

Understanding the Needs of Your Staff

What do your staff members want out of a job? We considered this question in Chapter Two, but now let's take a broader view.

Surveys often have shown a disparity between what people want out of a job and what their supervisors think they want. Many supervisors and managers rank money and job security at the top of the list of what they feel their staff want from a job. And yet, most staff surveys put money and job security somewhere between third place and sixth place behind such issues as appreciation for good work, recognition, feeling involved with the organization, and a comfortable work environment.

Does this disparity surprise you? We often forget what drove us when we were in our staff members' positions. For that matter, we may even forget what drives us in our current position. It's usually the same: supervisors seek more responsibility and recognition for a job well done, not just a raise.

Two psychologists, Abraham Maslow and Frederick Herzberg, have studied people's needs to explain the reasons behind them.

Abraham Maslow

Abraham Maslow developed what is known as the theory of self-actualization. Very simply stated, the theory of self-actualization describes the needs of people in terms of a hierarchy. Maslow's hierarchy moves from the most basic needs to higher needs: physical needs, safety/security, social/belonging needs, self esteem, and self-actualization needs. In other words, we must first meet our most basic needs— those at the bottom of the hierarchy—before our needs shift to a higher level.

. . . the theory of self-actualization describes the needs of people in terms of a hierarchy.

For example, a person who is starving and has no place to sleep is probably not as concerned with what people think about him as with eating and finding shelter. Those are basic needs. Once that person has established a steady diet and place to live (physical), he needs to feel safe and secure (safety/security). Then his needs move up the hierarchy. The person then wants to find a place in society and belong with others (social/belonging). Next, he becomes concerned with how he feels about himself (self-esteem). Finally, he wants to achieve his fullest potential (self-actualization).

In our society, the majority of people are near the top of the hierarchy. Maslow describes the top levels as self-realization and self-actualization. We respond to recognition, and a sense of responsibility and achievement, because our primary needs have been met.

Does this view make sense to you? Does it help explain the results of so many organization and staff surveys? Does it explain your own behavior on the job?

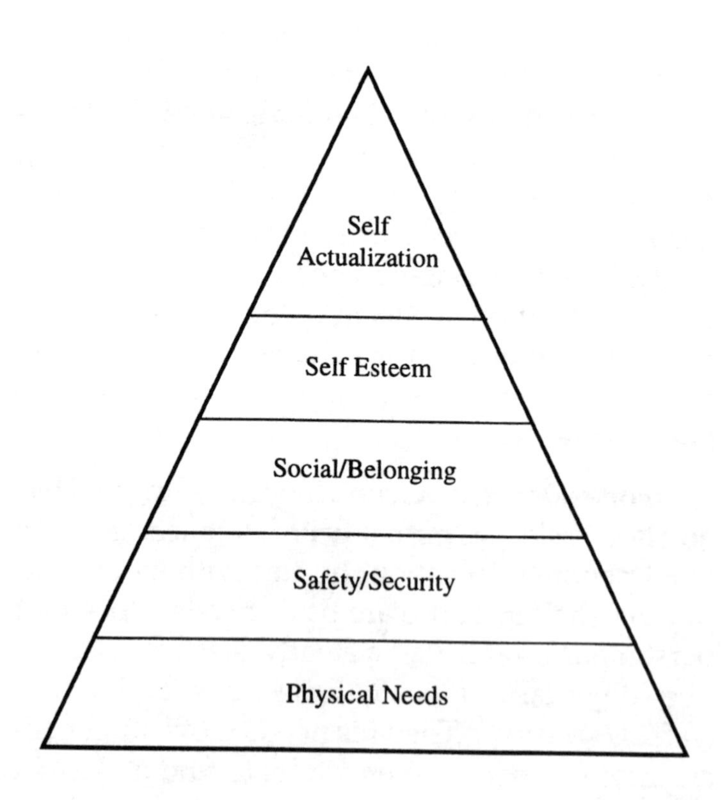

Take a Moment . . .

As we saw in Chapter Two, your staff have a variety of needs and goals that you need to consider. Some of the most common higher-level needs are listed below. Try to determine which needs are most important for your staff and for yourself. In other words, what do you or your staff need or what are you lacking?

- Safety/Security—need a sense of job security and stability; not too many changes; a stable work environment; like routine tasks.

Which staff members have this need and how does it show up on the job?

____

____

Do you have this need? If so, how does it show up on the job?

____

- Social/Belonging—need to be a part of the group, to fit in; like to get along with and interact with co-workers.

Which staff members have this need and how does it show up on the job?

____

____

Do you have this need? If so, how does it show up on the job?

____

Take a Moment *(continued)*

- Self-esteem—need to be recognized as someone important, to have status; like to be considered influential and a source of good ideas; want to be trusted to work alone; want to feel very confident.

Which staff members have this need and how does it show up on the job?

____

____

____

Do you have this need? If so, how does it show up on the job?

____

____

- Mature/Self-Actualizing—the ideal staff members. They blend a mix of curiosity and interest in what's going on and at the same time are willing to take charge of a task with a good deal of self-confidence; need recognition, opportunities to achieve, to take on more responsibility.

Which staff members have this need and how does it show up on the job?

____

____

____

Do you have this need? If so, how does it show up on the job?

____

Frederick Herzberg

Here's another view. Frederick Herzberg presents us with the two-factor theory. Simply stated, job elements are classified as one of two factors. They are:

- either *motivating factors*—things that motivate us,
- or *hygiene factors*—conditions that are basic and must be present.

For example, good lighting in your place of work is a hygiene factor. It must be present, but it doesn't motivate anyone to come to work. A promotion or recognition is a motivating factor. We work for those kinds of honors.

Interestingly enough, salaries are considered a hygiene factor. Would you go to work if your paycheck was not assured? It doesn't motivate us, but it has to be there. A new raise may be a motivating factor briefly, but the salary increase quickly becomes expected and, therefore, a hygiene factor.

. . . with the two-factor theory . . . job elements are classified as one of two factors. They are:

- ***motivating*** **or**
- ***hygiene.***

Take A Moment . . .

List four hygiene factors in your work environment.

____

____

____

____

Take a Moment *(continued)*

List four motivating factors available in your work environment.

____

____

____

Understanding the Needs of Your Organization

Your organization expects you to supervise people and the work they do. As a supervisor, you take direction from others and implement tasks through the people who work for you.

Your organization's expectations of you may include:

- **Staying aware of the big picture.** Don't focus only on your own department or immediate responsibilities. Be sensitive to what's going on in other departments and to meeting the needs of the organization as a whole.
- **Creating a productive environment for your staff.** Practicing good supervision skills that will lead to productive staff is a basic requirement for the job.
- **Making decisions on your own and exercising leadership and good judgment.**
- **Implementing new programs and methods while gaining staff acceptance.**
- **Communicating effectively with your staff to keep them informed about your**

organization's policies and procedures.

- **Teaching your staff to be effective at what they do and helping them develop their own skills.**

It's a tall order for any supervisor, but this list should be a part of your own job goals.

Take a Moment . . .

Are there any other expectations of your role as a supervisor—noted in your job description, expressed to you by your supervisor, or identified in your performance evaluation?

____

____

____

Look back at the work goals you set for yourself in Chapter One. Do they reflect all the expectations of a supervisor? Note here any expectations that need to be incorporated into your goals: __________________

____

____

____

Now incorporate them into your goals.

____

____

____

____

____

In Conclusion

Supervision is a challenging and rewarding job that combines many skills and talents. Like everything else, supervision skills and techniques will change and evolve. Stay on top of your profession by constantly improving your own skills. The complete supervisor is always on the lookout for ways to improve job performance, including his or her own methods of supervising.

Chapter Ten Review

1. True/False. Supervisors often think staff want one thing out of a job when they often want another.

2. List the basic needs identified by psychologist Abraham Maslow.

   ____

   ____

   ____

   ____

   ____

3. Define the factors identified by psychologist Frederick Herzberg.

   Hygiene ______________________

   ____

   ____

   Motivating_____________________

   ____

   ____

   ____

4. List four expectations that your organization may have for you as a supervisor.

____

____

____

____

Post Self-Assessment

So now how do you feel about being a supervisor? How do you feel about your ability to perform the job well? Take this self-assessment test and decide for yourself. Plan to work on the areas where you rate yourself as needing improvement.

	Always	Sometimes	Never	Score
1. I write a list of personal and work goals and keep it updated.	❑	❑	❑	____
2. I keep my goals prioritized in order of importance so that I know where I am headed.	❑	❑	❑	____
3. I know, from my staff's point of view, what is important to them in their work.	❑	❑	❑	____
4. I feel confident in directing the actions of the people who work for me.	❑	❑	❑	____
5. I am comfortable making decisions on my own.	❑	❑	❑	____
6. I feel comfortable communicating with staff.	❑	❑	❑	____
7. I feel comfortable communicating with my supervisor(s).	❑	❑	❑	____
8. I focus on developing the skills of my staff.	❑	❑	❑	____
9. I keep an open mind when making decisions that will affect my staff.	❑	❑	❑	____
10. I am careful not to take sides in disputes.	❑	❑	❑	____
11. When I make a decision, I think about its implications.	❑	❑	❑	____

	Always	Sometimes	Never	Score
12. I try to gain staff acceptance of my decisions without forcing them.	❑	❑	❑	____
13. When we implement a new procedure, I carefully observe how well it is working.	❑	❑	❑	____
14. I explain the reasons for a new procedure rather than just explaining that a new procedure exists.	❑	❑	❑	____
15. I am patient with staff when they are learning a new procedure.	❑	❑	❑	____
16. I build in contingency plans for new procedures in case they don't work.	❑	❑	❑	____
17. I always know how I'm spending my time and make sure that I use it effectively.	❑	❑	❑	____
18. I prioritize my work on a daily basis.	❑	❑	❑	____
19. I listen carefully to my staff.				
20. I am sensitive to cultural differences.	❑	❑	❑	____
21. I communicate clearly and am well understood by my staff:				
In writing	❑	❑	❑	____
Verbally	❑	❑	❑	____
22. When I hold a meeting, I plan the agenda in advance and let everyone know what it is.	❑	❑	❑	____

	Always	Sometimes	Never	Score
23. I prepare in advance for individual meetings or meetings with a group.	❑	❑	❑	____
24. I praise my staff when they do a good job.	❑	❑	❑	____
25. I avoid mixing praise and criticism.	❑	❑	❑	____
26. I keep personal issues out of criticism and focus only on behavior.	❑	❑	❑	____
27. I criticize in private only.	❑	❑	❑	____
28. I listen carefully when criticizing to hear the staff member's point of view.	❑	❑	❑	____
29. I make a conscious effort to delegate work to others so that they may learn.	❑	❑	❑	____
30. I am careful to delegate work that is best suited to staff.	❑	❑	❑	____
31. I set goals for staff when they take on new tasks.	❑	❑	❑	____
32. I use a variety of training methods to teach my staff new tasks.	❑	❑	❑	____
33. I appeal to the self-interest of my staff in wanting to do a better job.	❑	❑	❑	____
34. I am sensitive to my staff as individuals and try to help them meet their own work goals.	❑	❑	❑	____

	Always	Sometimes	Never	Score
35. I am sensitive to the needs of the organization and retain a big-picture perspective on organizational goals.	❑	❑	❑	_____
		Total Points		_____

How did you do? Where do you need to improve? To find your score, give yourself a 3 for each *Always*, a 2 for each *Sometimes*, and a 1 for each *Never*.

90 or higher: Congratulations! You're on your way to success as a supervisor.

76 89: You're above average and have developed some of the critical management and supervisory skills needed to become an excellent supervisor.

66 75: You're doing an acceptable job but could improve in some key areas.

65 or fewer: You still have work ahead of you to become comfortable at supervising.

Keep this workbook handy as a reference, and use it when you need help. Be sure to write and let us know how this workbook has helped you, and how we can help you foster your professional development in other areas.

American Correctional Association
Professional Development Department
4380 Forbes Boulevard Lanham, Maryland 20706-4322

http://www.corrections.com/aca e-mail: dianeg@aca.org

Answers to Chapter Reviews

Chapter One Review

1. **True.**
2. Common activities for supervisors include (choose two): *planning activities, hours, and scheduling; providing leadership and direction; managing or supervising others to make sure that work gets done; and taking responsibility for the performance of the people working for you.*
3. A *goal* is something to aim for, something you want to achieve. It's a clear statement of behavior you want.
4. Personality traits supervisors need include (choose four): *patience, tolerance, sensitivity, empathy, punctuality, and decisiveness.*
5. Common barriers to succeeding as a supervisor include (choose two): *too many goals, a lack of priorities, incomplete projects, and a lack of self-confidence.*

Chapter Two Review

1. The term *leadership* essentially means getting others to want to follow your direction and be productive in doing so.
2. The skills of leadership include (choose four): *being confident in your ability, having a desire to develop skills in others, being comfortable giving direction to others, and being able to communicate effectively, make decisions, trust your staff to do the job, and motivate people.*
3. The top five job motivators for most people are: *recognition for doing a good job, opportunities for advancement, trust, responsibility and respect.*
4. **False.** Titles can provide leadership, but they don't guarantee that the supervisor actually has leadership skills.

Chapter Three Review

1. The five steps to approaching a decision are:
   1. Be truly open-minded.
   2. Avoid taking sides.

   3. Recognize your own biases (preferences).
   4. Don't let titles or prestige influence your decision.
   5. Avoid "absolute" wording in your decision.

2. As you prepare to make a decision, you should ask yourself:
   1. Do I have enough information to make a decision?
   2. Does the problem require a decision?
   3. Am I the best person to make this decision?
   4. What will be the worst possible result if I make a wrong decision?

3. The three options in the decision making process are to *proceed, oppose, or take no action at all.*

4. The six key questions to ask when you are "selling" a decision are:
   1. What information should be provided to those people affected?
   2. Should it be in writing, and if so, how should I organize the information?
   3. Is my presentation of the decision phrased in language that will gain support for the decision?
   4. What negative responses might I expect?
   5. When and how will the information be presented to the staff involved?
   6. What questions are likely to come from supervisors and other staff when I present the decision?

Chapter Four Review

1. **False.** The majority of people are *not* risk takers.

2. Guidelines for implementing change effectively include (choose four):
   1. Make a decision and stick to it.
   2. Develop a plan.
   3. Plan each phase of the change.
   4. Examine possible alternatives to each step; draw up contingency plans.
   5. Monitor staff behavior to ensure that changes are implemented.
   6. Accept and plan for the results of the change.

3. The five steps for "selling"change to your staff are:
    1. Present the new idea to staff in clear, accessible language.
    2. Present your ideas in positive, sales-oriented language.
    3. As the change is implemented, stress your willingness to help staff members adapt.
    4. If the change is a major one, ask each staff member to tell you how he or she plans to handle it on the job.
    5. If the change has other unintended results, be open to reviewing what has occurred and to responding as needed.

4. To "sell" your ideas for change to your supervisors, present your ideas in clear, easy-to-understand language, both verbally and in writing. Use positive, sales-oriented language. Then, wait for your supervisors' decision. To influence that decision, be prepared to provide additional supportive information and even to negotiate on some points of your new plan.

Chapter Five Review

1. Common time-wasters are (choose six):
    1. Doing too many things at once; leaving tasks unfinished
    2. Poor communication with staff
    3. Procrastination
    4. No priorities for work tasks
    5. Unrealistic time estimates of projects
    6. Poor scheduling
    7. Too much attention to detail of other people's work
    8. Too many meetings
    9. Meetings run too long
    10. Solving staff members' personal problems
    11. Long phone conversations
    12. Doing my staff's work
    13. Poor communication with supervisors
    14. Too much paperwork with no clearly identified need

2. **True.**

3. **False.** Being busy has nothing to do with being productive. Maximizing how you spend your time means a great deal more.

4. **False.** You must be efficient at doing the right tasks. If you spend

most of your time doing tasks from your old job and very little time doing supervisory tasks, you won't be effective.

5. Techniques for better managing your time are (choose four):
   1. Make weekly and daily to-do lists in order of priority.
   2. Plan telephone calls in advance.
   3. Evaluate your time management several times during the day.
   4. Look at your personal list of major time-wasters.
   5. Plan what you are going to do at least one day ahead.
   6. Plan meetings—one-on-one or with a group—in advance.

Chapter Six Review

1. The *background* and *experience* of each listener influences what is being heard.
2. *Hearing* is the physical act of processing sounds. *Listening* is a blend of hearing and waiting, an intense connection with another person.
3. The seven steps for effective listening are:
   1. Ask questions.
   2. Concentrate.
   3. Listen for the main idea(s).
   4. Listen for the rationale behind what the other person is saying.
   5. Listen for key words.
   6. Organize what you hear in your own mind in a way that is logical for you.
   7. Take notes if the issue or request is complex.
4. Three *positive* gestures in the United States are: leaning forward, maintaining direct eye contact, and having open hands. Three *negative* gestures are: leaning away, folding arms over the chest, or backing away.
5. Guidelines for getting yourself heard include (choose five):
   1. Present one idea at a time.
   2. Keep it simple.
   3. Make it brief.
   4. Personalize what you are saying and present it to the individual.

5. Use the right tone of voice and the right body language for the situation.
6. Get acceptance of each idea you present.
7. Respond to the emotions of the people with whom you're talking.
8. Appreciate your listeners' concerns.
9. Encourage your listeners to express themselves.

6. Guidelines for effective writing include (choose three):

Commands the reader's attention
Generates reader's interest
Involves the reader
Prepares the reader to take action
Is reader-oriented
Is clear and concise
Is tactful and courteous
Has a conversational tone and the English is simple
Gives the reader useful information
Probably will produce the desired affect on the reader

Chapter Seven Review

1. The seven questions you should ask yourself before beginning a meeting are:
   1. What is the purpose of this meeting?
   2. How long should it take?
   3. What am I going to say and in what order?
   4. What is the outcome I want? What am I expecting the other person to do?
   5. How is the person(s) likely to react to what I'm going to say?
   6. What other topics are likely to come up, and am I prepared for them?
   7. How will I end the meeting?

2. The 12 rules for conducting a productive meeting are:
   1. Avoid a **meeting** if possible.
   2. Keep the group **small**.
   3. Give everyone an **agenda** in advance.
   4. Invite only those people who **really need** to attend.
   5. Start and end as soon as your **agenda** has been covered.

6. Keep the discussion **focused**.
7. Write down ideas and **repeat** them with slightly **different** phrasing.
8. If someone criticizes another, jump in **immediately** and rephrase the comment in a **more positive way**.
9. **Draw in** everyone.
10. Don't be afraid of **heated discussion** or **disagreement**.
11. Remain **calm** and **neutral**, no matter what happens.
12. Summarize **what was accomplished** and clarify **what action needs to be taken and by whom.**

3. How do you deal with each of the situations so that your meeting runs smoothly?
   A. *You hold a meeting to resolve problems relating to transporting offenders. But the topic drifts toward problems in a certain cellblock.*
   Ask questions related to the subject of the meeting.
   B. *You're conducting a meeting and two of your staff are dominating the discussion.*
   Ask questions or opinions of the silent attendees.
   C. *During a meeting, you accidentally call a new staff member by the wrong name.*
   Admit your mistake and apologize to the person.
   D. *Smith and Johnson are not participating in the discussion.*
   Ask Smith and Johnson for ideas or opinions.
   E. *You notice during a meeting that staff appear to be getting bored—you see tapping pens, eyes glaring at watches, eyes staring off into space, and bodies slumping in chairs.*
   Keep meetings focused and short to avoid boredom.
   F. *In the middle of your meeting, Randall and Vickers start arguing with each other over a point.*
   Encourage them to express what they're thinking, but be sure that they do not personally attack each other.

4. If someone else calls a meeting, you should:
   A. Do nothing but attend.
   B. Write down and submit ideas for the agenda.
   C. Critique the agenda and return it before the meeting.
   X D. Be prepared for the meeting.

Chapter Eight Review

1. The four tips for giving praise are:
   1. Mean what you say.
   2. Say what you mean, don't "pile it on."
   3. Balance your use.
   4. Use praise to provide encouragement.

2. **True.** Praise staff as close to the behavior as possible—to increase the chances of the behavior being repeated.

3. Guidelines for giving effective criticism include (choose three):
   - Limit your comments to the behavior.
   - Criticize as quickly as possible when you discover a problem.
   - Don't present criticism with praise.
   - Be considerate.
   - Don't trap or humiliate staff members.
   - Listen carefully to what the staff member has to say.

4. **False.** You should *never* criticize a staff member in front of other staff.

5. **False.** Written criticism is far more severe than verbal criticism and becomes part of the staff member's record.

6. The five steps for managing conflicts are:
   1. Take responsibility for dealing with conflict.
   2. Uncover, define, and discuss the real problem.
   3. Ask questions and listen!
   4. Set goals and create an action plan.
   5. Follow up.

7. Asking the right questions means:
   Ask **open-ended** questions.
   Choosing your **words** carefully.
   Follow up with **targeted probing questions** if the initial answer is not sufficient.

8. Listening successfully means:
   Listen **objectively** and with an **open** mind.
   Reassure the other person that you are interested in his or her **perception** of the situation.
   Offer **positive feedback** by **paraphrasing** (repeating in your own

words) what you've heard and following up with questions based on the new information.

Chapter Nine Review

1. Benefits of delegating tasks to staff include (choose three):
   1. Delegating work to others improves your time management and productivity.
   2. Delegating work is more efficient.
   3. Delegating work develops the skills and abilities of others.
   4. Delegation increases job satisfaction for your staff.
   5. It helps you better evaluate your staff.
2. The three reasons why supervisors are reluctant to delegate tasks to staff are:
   1. Less power and influence.
   2. Less control over the job.
   3. Giving up the "fun" stuff.
3. **False.** You cannot just delegate all of your tasks to staff. You must figure out which tasks best suit each individual staff member. Some tasks cannot be delegated to staff.
4. The three key rules for delegating work to staff are:
   1. Don't take an assignment back after you've delegated it.
   2. Encourage your staff to learn and make their own decisions about how to do the task.
   3. Make sure that you've clearly defined what you want your staff to do.

Chapter Ten Review

1. **True.** Supervisors often make wrong assumptions about staff's needs on the job.
2. The basic needs identified by psychologist Abraham Maslow are:
   1. Physical needs
   2. Safety/Security
   3. Social/Belonging
   4. Self-esteem
   5. Self-actualization

3. The factors identified by psychologist Frederick Herzberg are:
   Hygiene factors are conditions that are basic and must be present, such as good lighting in the workplace.
   Motivating factors are things that motivate us, such as a promotion or recognition.

4. Expectations that your organization may have for you as a supervisor include (choose four):
   1. Staying aware of the big picture.
   2. Creating a productive environment for your staff.
   3. Making decisions on your own and exercising leadership and good judgment.
   4. Implementing new programs and methods while gaining staff acceptance.
   5. Communicating effectively with your staff to keep them informed about your organization's policies and procedures.
   6. Teaching your staff to be effective at what they do and helping them develop their own skills.